Puzzlers' Choice
CROSSWORD

hinkler

hinkler

Published by Hinkler Books Pty Ltd
45–55 Fairchild Street
Heatherton Victoria 3202 Australia
www.hinkler.com.au

Design © Hinkler Books Pty Ltd 2013
© Lovatts Publications 2011, 2012

Cover design: Sam Grimmer
Typesetting: MPS Limited

ISBN: 978 1 7435 2018 5

Printed and bound in China

Puzzles

Crossword 1

ACROSS

1. Find
5. Bat's flight limb
7. Member of jury
8. Meditation art
9. Iridescent gem
10. Metal links
11. Most recent
13. Merriment
14. Gaped
18. Army students
21. Write by machine
22. Frozen drip
24. Cut into cubes
25. Small mountain
26. Smug moralist
27. Painter's tripod
28. Lock openers
29. Completes (crossword)

DOWN

1. Allegiance
2. Degrade
3. Remove (DVD) from player
4. Naturally grown
5. Treated unfairly
6. Closest
12. Seek damages from
15. Whenever
16. Pine tree leaves
17. Debate
19. Circle portion
20. Snow vehicles
22. Cult heroes
23. Drive forward

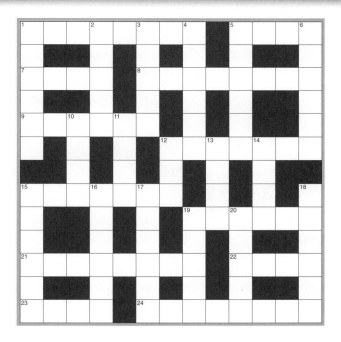

ACROSS
1. Multiplying by two
5. Grass section
7. Bung
8. Funny movies
9. Anglican parish priest
12. Raining heavily
15. Military school
19. Refused consent
21. Trilling
22. Tiny (version)
23. Riverside plant
24. Tunes

DOWN
1. Leave
2. Prejudiced person
3. Become liable for
4. Place bets
5. Monotony
6. Blending by melting
10. Unnatural sleep
11. Stare lustfully at
12. Plaything
13. Threat, do it or ...!
14. Towards interior of
15. Response
16. Touched lightly
17. Average
18. Acknowledges
19. Nocturnal watch
20. Measured duration of

Crossword 3

ACROSS
1. Rank
5. Wordless acting
7. Adversary
8. Tinted
9. Bridge length
10. Deserve
11. Becomes informed
13. Snake-like fish
14. Floats on current
18. Merriest
21. Speak indistinctly
22. Rang (of bells)
24. Outdo
25. Swarm
26. Japanese wrestling style
27. Ease off
28. Unkind
29. Strip bare

DOWN
1. Used oars
2. Scanning device
3. Judges
4. Clothed in
5. Enigma
6. Childhood disease
12. Louse egg
15. Allay
16. Inferno battler
17. Out of the ordinary
19. Chopping tool
20. Immature frog
22. Kept supplying
23. Incendiary crime

ACROSS
1. Arctic (region)
7. Exonerated
8. Leg bone
10. Improve efficiency of
12. Proximity
14. Ewe's young
16. Dock
17. Clearly expressed
20. Trees retaining foliage
23. Rescued
24. More slender
25. Giant monsters

DOWN
1. Benefactor
2. Line of rotation
3. Gifted
4. Weaving machines
5. Evasion
6. Verb modifier
9. Make amends
11. Medical support worker
13. Gender
15. Tribal groups
16. Nauseated
18. Barters
19. Spy, secret ...
21. Optic organs
22. Performed in opera

Crossword 5

ACROSS

1. Mechanical devices
5. Spun
7. Insect larva
8. Public addresses
9. Hire contracts
12. Frisks (about)
15. Skilled worker
19. Loaded (suitcase)
21. Went back over
22. Tiny arachnid
23. Obscene
24. Unit of pronunciation

DOWN

1. Magnates
2. Great Depression drifters
3. Alcoves
4. Ice performer
5. Blanch
6. Long exam answers
10. Border on
11. Snake-like fish
12. Grenade trigger
13. Zone
14. Wine bottle plug
15. Celestial
16. Innate
17. Early counting instrument
18. Stick (to)
19. Bike footrest
20. Punctuation mark

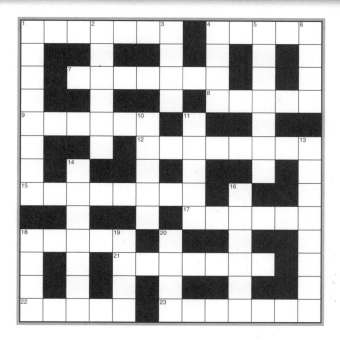

ACROSS

1. Male spouse
4. Allude
7. Mainly
8. Room
9. Flung
12. Improper
15. Seizing
17. Executes (law)
18. Looks longingly
21. Tires
22. Child's toy, ... bear
23. Endless

DOWN

1. Emerging from egg
2. For, on ... of
3. Resist
4. Sunbeams
5. Had buoyancy
6. Lariat
10. Finger or toe
11. Wise saying
13. Unsuspecting
14. Blinded by light
16. Profession
18. Central idea
19. Move to & fro
20. Celebrity status

Crossword 7

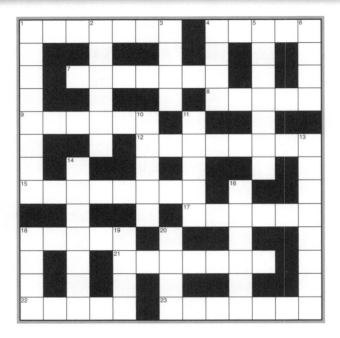

ACROSS

1. Small quantity
4. Fail (of computer)
7. Antiquated
8. Rogue
9. Harry Potter is one
12. 12-month-old horse
15. Glistens
17. Gives up
18. Pledged
21. Speaking publicly
22. Display frames
23. Habitable

DOWN

1. Major roads
2. Main fin
3. Seep
4. Male bird
5. Of water
6. Flexible pipe
10. Dutch levee banks
11. Common flower
13. Precious rock
14. Temporary camp
16. Abdominal rupture
18. Night sky object
19. Assents with head
20. Become boring

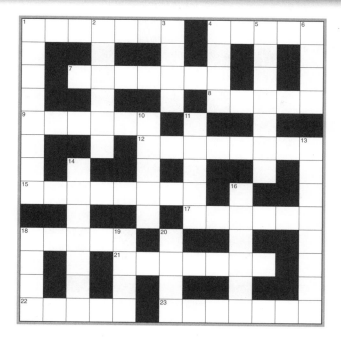

ACROSS
1. Mosquito-borne fever
4. Freshly
7. Tempted
8. Written tests
9. Delivery task
12. Instances
15. Restate (position)
17. Frightened
18. Fire fragment
21. Without weapons
22. Expel
23. Mythical beast

DOWN
1. Assassin
2. Yearly
3. Bridge span
4. Plant stem lump
5. Feminine
6. Shrill barks
10. Discourage
11. Uses lure
13. Sporting parachutist
14. Sauerkraut vegetable
16. Clothing tags
18. Fencing sword
19. Weakest in litter
20. Moderately hot

Crossword 9

ACROSS

1. Detained, held in ...
4. Spin
7. Attire
8. Australian marsupial
9. Sings Swiss alpine-style
12. Mixed alcoholic drink
15. Gain degree
17. Numb
18. Hollywood prize, Academy ...
21. Craved, ... for
22. Was painful
23. Detected

DOWN

1. Conveying
2. Refilled, ... up
3. Wool
4. Slow gait
5. Tropical lizards
6. Tibetan monk
10. Food remnant
11. Behaved
13. Fired (missile)
14. Nasal discharge
16. Photographer's tool
18. Greenish blue
19. Tinted
20. Lamenting cry

ACROSS

1. Inborn
5. Cajole
7. Mutineer
8. Mortuary table
9. Nervous
10. Greek letter
11. Despise
13. Steals from
14. Italian sausage
18. Of medicinal plants
21. Burial vault
22. Lyrics
24. Frostily
25. Put in the ground (of seeds)
26. Cow flesh
27. Body part
28. Requests, ... for
29. Affable

DOWN

1. Disparaging remarks
2. Monastery superior
3. Wear away
4. Put an end to (law)
5. More distinct
6. Branch of mathematics
12. Smoked pork
15. Loving
16. Pure white animals
17. Encroach
19. The self
20. Lecherous
22. Competing
23. Ocean liner bedroom

Crossword 11

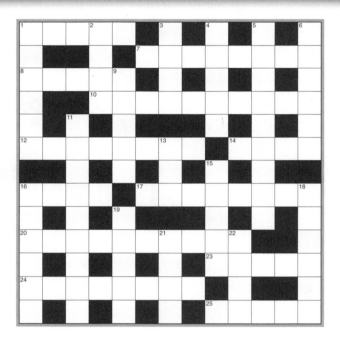

ACROSS

1. Arrives at wharf
7. Climb hurriedly
8. Lower leg joint
10. Sickening
12. Identify disease
14. Thoughtful
16. Drug (horse)
17. Pirates' hoard
20. Car's lamps
23. Cultural symbols
24. Frozen shipping hazards
25. Aggravated

DOWN

1. Hung in folds
2. Pottery furnace
3. Treads the boards
4. Gold purity unit
5. Blithely unconcerned
6. Pleaded
9. Merits
11. Air force fighters
13. Respectful address
15. Desert plants
16. Mexican flower
18. Wiped out
19. Adjust
21. Chokes
22. Disfiguring mark

ACROSS
1. Embark, get ...
5. Appropriately
7. Monastery church
8. Prank
9. Orderly
10. River-mouth triangle
11. Imprudent
13. Spicy honey liquor
14. Scolded repeatedly
18. Slashed
21. Pare
22. Fighting instrument
24. Ultra-virile
25. Opposed to
26. Grecian pots
27. Set of beliefs
28. Ship's floor
29. Perspiration-soaked

DOWN
1. Postpone (court case)
2. Sports stadium
3. Adam Sandler comedy, Big ...
4. Eliminate
5. Forceful
6. Fluid loss
12. Fish eggs
15. Put in order
16. Promotional device
17. Water channels
19. Affirmative vote
20. Ruling family
22. Golfer, Tiger ...
23. Mistreat

Crossword 13

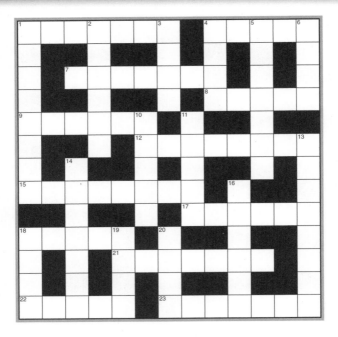

ACROSS

1. Copy
4. More aged
7. Ship's master
8. Fire fragment
9. Tropical virus, ... Fever
12. Restate (position)
15. Search in refuse
17. Lounged
18. Candle strings
21. In direction of
22. Blunder
23. Interfered

DOWN

1. Reshapes
2. Prone
3. Sound boosters
4. Storybook monster
5. Tennis pairs
6. Raise (children)
10. Squeezed (out)
11. Desert beast
13. Offered
14. Parade participant
16. Plain-spoken
18. Worker's income
19. Commotion
20. Did breaststroke

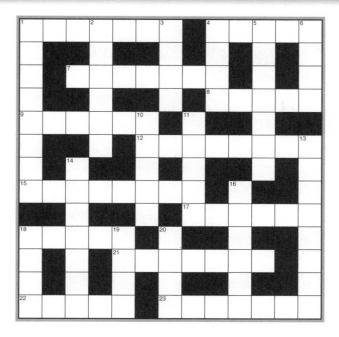

ACROSS

1. Legally kill
4. Emerge (of new chick)
7. Fire from job
8. Detected sound
9. For each, per ...
12. Mimes
15. Submissiveness
17. Shocking ordeal
18. Skewered meat dish
21. Drank
22. Not hollow
23. Survived

DOWN

1. Expulsion of evil spirits
2. Medical rooms
3. Lengthy movie
4. Peace & quiet
5. In direction of
6. Weeded
10. Felt pain
11. Midriff
13. Discarded
14. Women's court sport
16. Tiers
18. Young goats
19. Flying animal
20. Woodwind instrument

Crossword 15

ACROSS
1. Choux treat, chocolate ...
5. Angler's worm
7. Degrade
8. Havana is there
9. Air passage
10. Precise
11. Swapped
13. Fleur-de-lis
14. Spiced sausage
18. Took notice of
21. ... A to B
22. Piled
24. Prepared
25. Ancestry, family ...
26. Languish
27. Beauty shop
28. Hit sharply
29. The aorta is one

DOWN
1. Thrills
2. Hollywood prize, Academy ...
3. Scraped (leaves)
4. Nasal discharge
5. Nightly ritual, ... story
6. Slope
12. Horror film, *A Nightmare on ... Street*
15. In-flight attendants
16. Side of chair
17. In perfect conditions
19. Lamb's mother
20. Frail with age
22. 'Laughing' scavenger
23. Allow in

ACROSS
1. Blissful
5. Sharpen
7. Fill to overflowing
8. Spanish dance style
9. Stages
12. Titled men
15. Deer meat
19. Wild feline animals
21. Numbers
22. Pig fat
23. Gape
24. Dimness

DOWN
1. Apart from
2. Camel's mounds
3. Starched neck frills
4. Pastel stick
5. Weeding
6. Wears away
10. Soon
11. Supplements, ... out
12. Relatives
13. Very black
14. Prank
15. Futilely
16. Imprison during war
17. Ahead
18. Incidental comments
19. Light-ray tool
20. Synthetic fabric

Crossword 17

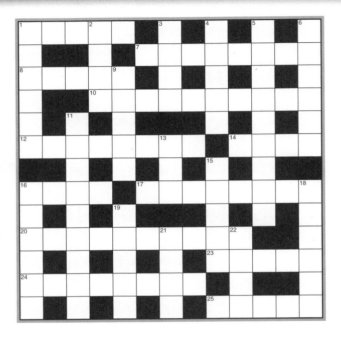

ACROSS
1. Privileged class
7. Former soldiers
8. Edible organs
10. Horseracing track
12. Entitling
14. Done breaststroke
16. Tasks
17. Scraps
20. Pop instrumentalists
23. Finnish steam bath
24. Highly charged
25. River-mouth land

DOWN
1. Develop
2. Rupture
3. Measure (out)
4. Furnishing scheme
5. Diminishing
6. Admiration
9. Large spoon
11. Partly cooked
13. Gesture of assent
15. Radiates
16. Sharply serrated
18. Musical composition
19. Taunts
21. Curved-bill bird
22. Auction

ACROSS

1. Duck's call
7. Sliding out of control
8. Church table
10. Enticement
12. Floor hatch
14. Volcanic flow
16. Labels
17. Small brimless hat
20. Without commander
23. Disliked
24. Before birth
25. Son or daughter

DOWN

1. Daintily odd
2. Jacket
3. Jump rope
4. Notions
5. Watchfulness
6. Meeting schedule
9. Prepared
11. Dialects
13. Acorn bearer
15. Gash
16. Dutch bulb flowers
18. Cushioned
19. Blossom part
21. Hop
22. Silk band

Crossword 19

ACROSS
1. Percussionists
5. Perform again
7. Tiny amount
8. Riches
9. Unfasten
12. Walked like duck
15. Propels canoe
19. Staggered
21. Supplied funds for
22. Dreary
23. Rounded roof
24. Startle

DOWN
1. Bores
2. Grumbles
3. Pointy-featured
4. Layers
5. Woken
6. Unseated
10. Had to repay
11. Tea, ... Grey
12. Used to be
13. Springboard descent
14. Sit lazily
15. Inflated, ... up
16. Give (to charity)
17. Throws out
    (of house)
18. Fit to be eaten
19. Equestrian
20. Senior

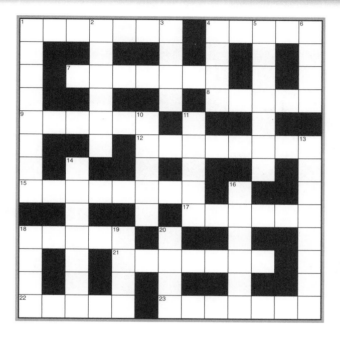

ACROSS

1. Power plant, ... reactor
4. Lukewarm
7. Eighth of mile
8. Wooden spike
9. Insult
12. Succumbing
15. Successive order
17. More precious
18. Vocal sound
21. Slackly
22. Study tables
23. Talk about

DOWN

1. Broadcasting companies
2. Noisier
3. Street uprising
4. Pulls
5. Egyptian burial building
6. Springboard descent
10. Expiring
11. Distributed, ... out
13. Connoisseurs
14. Wriggles
16. Pungent bulb
18. Did battle (with)
19. Deer
20. Nourishment

Crossword 21

ACROSS
1. Supplied funds for
5. Dam
7. Smear
8. Rissole
9. Acidity paper
12. Calling (of donkey)
15. Underground railway systems
19. Perspires
21. Intermittently
22. Speechless
23. Aromatic herb
24. Cannier

DOWN
1. Violin
2. Soundtrack CD
3. Arrives
4. Desk compartment
5. Unstable
6. Reigning
10. Burial chamber
11. Forearm bone
12. Commuter vehicle
13. Affirm
14. Novel thought
15. Rode on wave
16. Dire
17. Gives way
18. Map pressure line
19. Wilier
20. Bequeath

ACROSS

1. Leave empty
5. Sets of tools
7. Magnitude
8. Without sensation
9. Every single
10. Pale with shock
11. Sprightly
13. Lambs' mothers
14. Scrape away
18. Tardiest
21. Wild feline animal
22. Frail
24. Likeness
25. Seep
26. Arm bone
27. Scottish fabric
28. Remain
29. Military gesture

DOWN

1. Tom Cruise movie,
   ... Sky
2. Leisurely walk
3. Composition
4. Shy
5. Most enthusiastic
6. Entry passes
12. Was ahead of
15. Trade ban
16. Nervous tension
17. Got free
19. Beer
20. Juvenile
22. Prolonged quarrels
23. Evenly balanced

Crossword 23

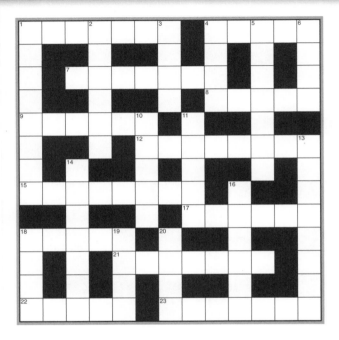

ACROSS
1. Siberian dogs
4. Respond
7. Towards the front
8. Conservative
9. Stared rudely
12. Logically presented
15. Skywatch
17. Radio crackle
18. Surrenders
21. Tired
22. Unsteady
23. Unrealistic person

DOWN
1. Six-sided figures
2. Raps
3. Hoax
4. Frees
5. Gets
6. Narrated
10. Fear greatly
11. Helium & hydrogen
13. Learn
14. Of the heart
16. Photographer's tool
18. Singe
19. Move to & fro
20. Praise highly

Crossword 24

ACROSS
1. Sinew
5. Post of doorway
7. Had to repay
8. Public speeches
9. Personify
12. Clearness
15. Most considerate
19. Was unsuccessful
21. Purgative
22. Leak out
23. Open valley
24. Paraffin oil

DOWN
1. Hooped
2. Of hearing
3. Black wood
4. Ride
5. Furniture maker
6. Industriously
10. Coffee seed
11. Eat
12. Carve
13. Charismatic glow
14. Object of worship
15. Assassinated
16. Prescribed amount
17. Decrease in size
18. Stick (to)
19. More independent
20. Symbolic pictures

Crossword 25

ACROSS
1. Living being
5. Inner hand part
7. Predatory canine
8. Of the home
9. Automatic (action)
12. Ocean liners or freighters
15. Put (sword) in scabbard
19. Steel support beam
21. Special event
22. Coarse file
23. Solitary
24. Mischievous imps

DOWN
1. Ahead
2. Terrible
3. Tabulated list
4. Speak indistinctly
5. Shoves
6. Tropical parrots
10. Destiny
11. Revise (text)
12. Compete
13. Indian gown
14. Children's writer, ... Blyton
15. Parchment roll
16. Burning out of control
17. Wishing
18. Vineyard crop
19. Magic lamp spirit
20. Pastoral

ACROSS

1. Ewe's offspring
7. Numerous
8. Baker's loaf
10. Convalescent home
12. Overpowered by sound
14. Satirical sketch
16. Achievement
17. Most comical
20. Taxi occupants
23. Slight error
24. Renew (energies)
25. Representative

DOWN

1. Hit ball high
2. Lingerie items
3. Bass brass instrument
4. Got up from chair
5. Tiny drops (of rain)
6. Allow
9. Titled ladies
11. Canvas shoulder-bag
13. Tall bird
15. Angry growl
16. Leave
18. Natural gift
19. Embarked on
21. Rock concerts
22. Performed in opera

Crossword 27

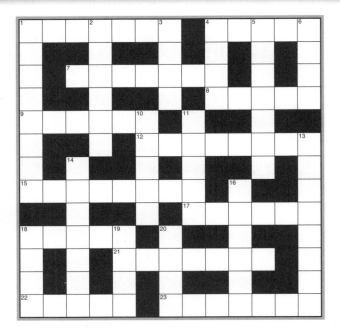

ACROSS
1. Raided
4. Tin or iron
7. Ocean-liner waiter
8. Greatly please
9. Yacht basin
12. Advantageously
15. Accompanied
17. Grab
18. Gentle prod
21. Catching (thief)
22. Timidly
23. Walks wearily

DOWN
1. Very personal
2. Achieve
3. College supervisor
4. Style
5. Wide pedal
6. Reside
10. Female relatives
11. Riverside plants
13. Face veils
14. Sourness
16. Arrived (of day)
18. Assents with head
19. Jealousy
20. Illegally help

ACROSS
1. Custodian
5. Extinct bird
7. Festive occasion
8. Least flexible
9. Excused
12. Curling (of mist)
15. Gland secretion
19. High seas robber
21. Slaughter
22. Back of neck
23. Citrus peel
24. In an instant

DOWN
1. Prevented from speaking
2. Kingdom
3. Fabric insert
4. Affixed with spikes
5. Dexterously
6. Choosing
10. At any time
11. Horseback sport
12. Sight organ
13. Imported food shop
14. Tiny amount
15. Carpenter's tool
16. Formed a crowd
17. Sibling's daughters
18. Religious dissent
19. Beg
20. Remove soap from

Crossword **29**

ACROSS
1. Essential nutrients
5. Thyme or sage
7. Volcanic matter
8. Approaching
9. Barely
12. Sold on street
15. Water-main outlet
19. Smother
21. Unstable (of chemical)
22. Robe
23. Lose (fur)
24. International agreements

DOWN
1. Degree of loudness
2. Mindful
3. Sense of the absurd
4. Safe
5. Buzzed monotonously
6. Planted microphones in
10. Rip violently
11. Tibetan priest
12. Coal mine
13. Musical piece for two
14. Block of bread
15. Slices down the middle
16. Hold back (growth)
17. Naturist
18. Creatures
19. Military blockade
20. Gold brick

ACROSS
1. Pattern of small tiles
5. The one there
7. Lift with effort
8. Reflected sound
9. Diplomacy
10. The Press
11. Evades (capture)
13. Tidy
14. Price list
18. Recommence
21. Body fluid lump
22. Stings
24. Satellite path
25. Premonition
26. Fencing sword
27. Older of two
28. Happy
29. Up-to-date

DOWN
1. Most submissive
2. Sidestep
3. Buddies
4. Less punctual
5. Lockjaw
6. Praise
12. Folklore creature
15. Atrocious
16. Chanted
17. Outlaws
19. Deciduous tree
20. Facing the rising sun
22. Violent weather
23. Reform

Crossword 31

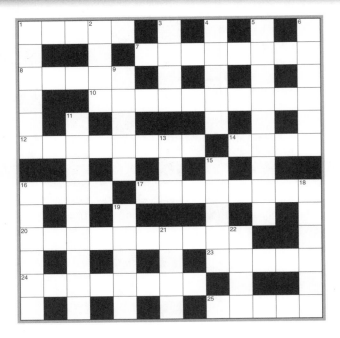

ACROSS
1. Searches for
7. Cumbersome
8. Upper leg
10. Sixtieth, ..., eightieth
12. Boarded ship
14. Long-necked bird
16. Puncture with knife
17. Acted treacherously
20. Intensified
23. Italian food
24. Of musical drama
25. Aptitude

DOWN
1. Lampooning comedy
2. Vats
3. A single time
4. Dirt
5. Narrow paths between buildings
6. Constrictor snake
9. Listens to
11. Polishing substances
13. Ram's mate
15. Move slowly
16. Teacher's workplace
18. Fine point
19. Common cereal
21. Revise (text)
22. Unpleasantly damp

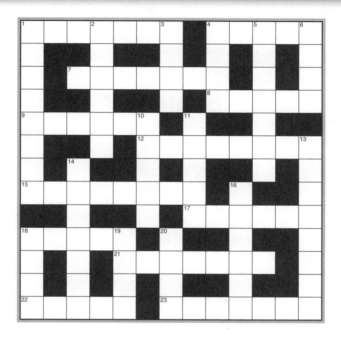

ACROSS
1. Coastal lakes
4. Copy outline of
7. Lost
8. Canadian gold rush region
9. Verb modifier
12. Not merited
15. Cattle charge
17. Emotional shock
18. Banjo sound
21. Sloping typeface
22. Marks as correct
23. Spanned

DOWN
1. Gymnasts outfits
2. Antipasto items
3. Fraud
4. Neaten
5. Emerges from sleep
6. Actor, ... McGregor
10. Consumer
11. Besieged
13. Left
14. Extremist
16. Spoiled (of butter)
18. Horse pace
19. Concert tour bookings
20. Post of doorway

Crossword 33

ACROSS
1. Expeditions
5. In this place
7. Uterus
8. Fortified wines
9. Finally
12. Expressionless
15. Tribal chief
19. Straighten
21. Poised (on the edge)
22. Resound
23. Fragrant type of tea, ... Grey
24. Rapidly

DOWN
1. Sapphires & diamonds
2. Mechanical man
3. Composition
4. Veer
5. Threw hard
6. Naval flag
10. Asian sauce bean
11. Weaving apparatus
12. Lair
13. Similar
14. Wan
15. Walk lamely
16. Come off tracks
17. Chinese calculator
18. Foolishness
19. Uncalled-for
20. Animal strain

ACROSS

1. Unstable (of chemical)
5. Object of worship
7. Towards interior of
8. Straw-roofed (cottage)
9. Commander
12. Sheep pelts
15. Revised
19. Genetically copied
21. Leaving empty
22. Govern
23. Actor, ... Nolte
24. Accentuates

DOWN

1. Futilely
2. Audibly
3. Place in crypt
4. Tooth covering
5. Earnings
6. Ski chalets
10. Amongst
11. Prepare (newspaper)
12. Short-lived trend
13. Wicked
14. Maize
15. Irregular
16. Go on offensive
17. Covets
18. Vipers
19. Tobacco product
20. Giant monsters

Crossword **35**

ACROSS
1. Caper
5. Forearm bone
7. Enthusiastic devotion
8. Straw-roofed (cottage)
9. Angrier
12. Dances (of horse)
15. Conveyance
19. Zoo custodian
21. Increased
22. Tulip or daffodil
23. Sudden invasion
24. Headfirst descent (4,4)

DOWN
1. Allergy rash
2. Suffered
3. Change
4. Travel cheat, fare ...
5. Marine animal, sea ...
6. Examines (accounts)
10. Morse symbols, dot & ...
11. Narrative poem
12. Pastry dish
13. Wheel shaft
14. Crack (of lip)
15. Thin covering
16. Water-bound area
17. Heavy (heart)
18. Triple
19. Personal glory
20. Lodge firmly

Crossword 36

ACROSS

1. Unspoken
5. Hats
7. Take place
8. Tulip or daffodil
9. Sinister
10. Din
11. Finds out
13. Mountain top
14. Vicious
18. Partition
21. Drove fast
22. Thing
24. Atlantic or Pacific
25. Mutilate
26. Door handle
27. Summon up
28. Eager
29. Neatly

DOWN

1. Unlatches
2. Fossil resin
3. Ups & ...
4. Is frugal
5. Clinging vine
6. Gorilla or monkey
12. Scold persistently
15. Pacify
16. Stomach
17. Imperial ruler
19. Young bear
20. Remarkably
22. Beginning (of illness)
23. Jested

Crossword 37

ACROSS
1. Inhibit
5. Pierce with dagger
7. Large chunk
8. Hiker's pack
9. Voluntarily, of one's own ...
12. Butting
15. Provoked
19. Unfasten (door)
21. In these times
22. Cavort
23. Venison animal
24. Even temper

DOWN
1. Scoundrel
2. Off-limits
3. Peeved
4. Shocking ordeal
5. Method
6. Cooking in oven
10. Fashionable
11. Floating log platform
12. Pole
13. Cry in pain
14. Towards interior of
15. Steam-pressed
16. Injure
17. Pitch tent
18. Paper fastener
19. Overturn
20. River vessel

ACROSS

1. Brews
5. Tibetan priest
7. Volcanic flow
8. Leaping over
9. Swiss cottage
12. Played the lead
15. Suspended
19. Spurn
21. Giving therapy to
22. Face covering
23. Shoe cord
24. Architectural overhaul

DOWN

1. Unbleached cotton
2. Move on hands & knees
3. Envy
4. Eject (liquid)
5. Pig's young
6. Sharply bent
10. Yemeni port
11. Wicked
12. Sorrowful
13. Competent
14. Fragrant flower
15. Of teeth
16. Lubricate
17. Weirder
18. Taken by thief
19. Went on rampage
20. Dances to rock & roll

Crossword 39

ACROSS
1. Elaborately
5. Storybook monster
7. Sacred vow
8. Crime against humanity
9. In short supply
12. Magazine issue
15. Deadlock
19. Pungent bulbs
21. Young children
22. Arm or leg
23. Skillets
24. Able to read & write

DOWN
1. Woodwind musician
2. Hate
3. Golfer's two under par
4. Pulled sharply
5. Of the supernatural
6. Ten, ..., twelve
10. On the summit of
11. Babies' beds
12. December 31, New Year's ...
13. Ferrous metal
14. Inside
15. Foot arch
16. Residences
17. Piglet's cry
18. Serviceable
19. Start (of disease)
20. Lazy person

ACROSS
1. Posted
5. Enquires
7. Leavening agent
8. Average
9. Diplomacy
10. Light push
11. Crowd
13. Spike
14. Lettuce dishes
18. Couturier's drawing
21. Polluted air
22. Actor, ... Depardieu
24. Ruined Inca city, ... Picchu
25. Loyal
26. Slay
27. Requirements
28. Calm (sea)
29. Lobs

DOWN
1. 60-second periods
2. State of suspension
3. Becoming extinct, ... out
4. Loitered
5. Is present at
6. Striking with foot
12. Assent with head
15. Fleet's senior rank
16. Supplement
17. Aghast
19. Use frugally, ... out
20. Small lumps
22. Hotel patron
23. Lawn tools

Crossword 41

ACROSS
1. Transgressed
5. Stupefy
7. Oarsman
8. Be frightened of
9. Australian gemstone
10. A second time
11. Reclaim
13. Ferrous metal
14. Italian sausage
18. Absorb (food)
21. Net fabric
22. Skimmed on ice
24. Pass into law
25. Night sky object
26. Nip
27. Edit (text)
28. Tinted
29. Crest

DOWN
1. African wildlife tours
2. Skin sensor
3. Sleeping vision
4. Perspired
5. Humming tunelessly
6. Passionate believers
12. Deciduous tree
15. Adroitly
16. Clung (to)
17. Pierced with spear
19. Printing fluid
20. Most orderly
22. Collar fasteners
23. Soundtrack CD

ACROSS
1. Game fowl
5. Shipment
7. Wrinkle
8. Removed (badge)
9. Sewing tool
12. Postal destination
15. Jostled
19. Accommodated
21. Delivered sermon
22. Cat-o'-nine-tails
23. Complete again
24. Balances

DOWN
1. Heaping
2. Correct
3. Blue shade
4. Refilled, ... up
5. Lengthier
6. Evades
10. Listening organs
11. Sit idly
12. Emergency medicine, first ...
13. Extinct bird
14. Supplements, ... out
15. Picnic basket
16. Red salad fruit
17. Inscribes
18. Takes in (child)
19. Leafy fence
20. Unmarried

Crossword 43

ACROSS
1. Prosperous
5. Long tale
7. Defrost
8. Embroiled
9. Close at hand
12. File holders
15. Information sheet
19. Book, Anne Of Green ...
21. Replies
22. Heavy metal
23. Very small
24. Sheds

DOWN
1. Performing
2. Drop (prices)
3. All
4. Red salad fruit
5. Took place after
6. Military students
10. Opera song
11. Male elephant
12. Overweight
13. Expelled magma
14. Sinister
15. Discovered
16. Limp
17. Became worthy of
18. Stage whispers
19. Helium & hydrogen
20. Light timber

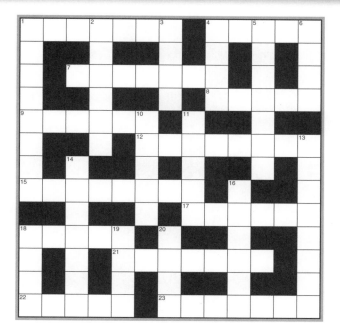

ACROSS
1. Card game
4. Relating to speech
7. Behave as glutton
8. Knowledge tests
9. Scowled
12. Granting
15. Most immature
17. Frightened
18. Supply sparingly
21. Hug
22. Female title
23. Herring relative

DOWN
1. Class
2. Verb modifier
3. Discontinued (project)
4. Cast ballot
5. Made of clay
6. Bottle tops
10. Calendar entries
11. Adds seasoning to
13. Leadership
14. Certified (accounts)
16. Bad (of butter)
18. Appear
19. Hair-wave treatment
20. Wading bird

Crossword **45**

ACROSS

1. Bringing on (birth)
5. Body's lower extremities
7. Girl's plaything
8. Immobility
9. Patronage
12. Most cherished
15. Regional speech
19. Arrange (troops)
21. Lawsuit petitioner
22. Carpentry spike
23. Citrus peel
24. Subtracted

DOWN

1. Charge with crime
2. Dim
3. Colloquial saying
4. Quick look
5. Male parent
6. Rent payer
10. Asian sauce bean
11. Double-reed instrument
12. Speckle
13. Area measurement
14. Sinister
15. Australian currency unit
16. Imposed (tax)
17. Craven person
18. Rode bicycle
19. Loved excessively, ... on
20. Sudden overwhelming anxiety

ACROSS

1. Connective tissue
5. Injure with horns
7. Insincere (of speech)
8. Decontaminates
9. Agreeably
12. Swings up & down
15. Mixed together
19. Frothed
21. Small firearms
22. Snatch
23. Prosecuted
24. Body of aircraft

DOWN

1. Map key
2. Stroll
3. Containing nothing
4. Monarch's seat
5. Blunders
6. Follows on
10. Sweetly endearing
11. Pig fat
12. Melancholy
13. Reflected sound
14. Tiny particle
15. Cleanses (wound)
16. Required
17. Overwhelm
18. Fit to eat
19. Hunger strikes
20. Guardian spirit

Crossword 47

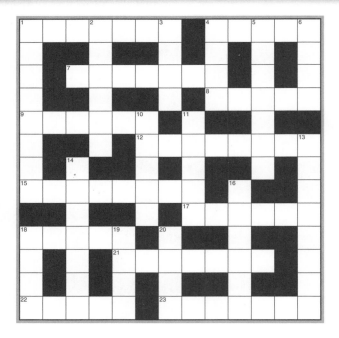

ACROSS
1. Humiliated
4. Placed in an aviary
7. Real
8. Deceptive move
9. Mutilated
12. Green gems
15. Leave place of danger
17. Clambered up
18. Corn husks
21. Relaxation time
22. Lifting device
23. Slavery

DOWN
1. Put together
2. Warning bells
3. Barrel
4. Young cow
5. Largest primate
6. Song for two voices
10. Prohibit
11. Annoys
13. Combination of symptoms
14. Card game
16. Excluded
18. Smartly-groomed
19. Duct
20. Arm or leg

ACROSS

1. Dramatic conclusion
5. Actor, Robert De ...
7. Lead-in
8. Mausoleum
9. Durable timber
10. Haul strenuously
11. Weasel-like animal
13. Dappled
14. Jousting weapons
18. Humble
21. Musical symbol
22. Skewers of meat
24. Picture border
25. Storybook monster
26. Outside limit
27. Majestic
28. Exploits
29. Moves furtively

DOWN

1. Ominous
2. Fossil resin
3. Octet number
4. Layer
5. Jotting book
6. Library patrons
12. December 31,
 New Year's ...
15. Claims
16. Money stores
17. Unusual
19. Dedicatory poem
20. Fringed cords
22. Ships' spines
23. Lose blood

Crossword 49

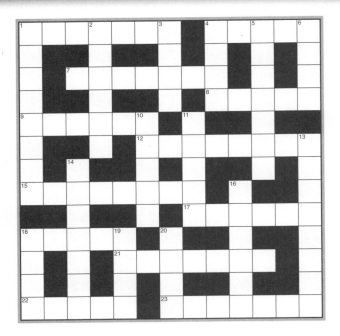

ACROSS
1. Worked (dough)
4. Female zebras
7. Refrain (from)
8. Hanker
9. Congenital
12. Fearless
15. Aspiring movie queens
17. Guttural
18. Geological division
21. Word puzzle
22. Shelled gastropod
23. Smiled smugly

DOWN
1. Massacres
2. Reddish-brown
3. Cult actor, James ...
4. Numerous
5. Absconder
6. Ignore
10. Deceived
11. Low wetland
13. No longer living
14. Portable rocket-launcher
16. Oriental market
18. Farm produce
19. Greet
20. Gently touches

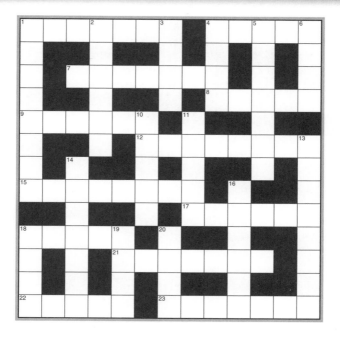

ACROSS

1. Opening
4. Proverb
7. Less abundant
8. Remove completely
9. Delivered, ... over
12. Cellophane covers
15. Role models
17. Harrowing ordeal
18. Compass point
21. Oblivious
22. Bread-raising agent
23. Suited

DOWN

1. Surpassed in excellence
2. Building's exterior
3. Every single
4. Land unit
5. Displayed
6. Alternatively, or ...
10. Live
11. Hips to ribs region
13. Exerted (oneself)
14. Spice
16. Textile, woven ...
18. Admiral's command
19. Stalk prey
20. Coconut tree

Crossword 51

ACROSS
1. Begs
5. Second-hand
7. Puts pressure (on)
8. Remake
9. Deception
10. Burn brightly
11. Shatters
13. Lamented
14. Consuming food
18. Cruelty
21. Bridge length
22. Nastier
24. Weight measure
25. Insect larva
26. Speak to God
27. Stone overhang
28. At a standstill
29. Builds

DOWN
1. Simple story lesson
2. Smell
3. Mortuary tables
4. Curved fruits
5. Escorted (to seat)
6. Pencil rubbers
12. Relatives
15. Eagerly desired
16. Disgraceful
17. Hand bomb
19. Trump card
20. Sufferers for cause
22. Fracas
23. More than enough

ACROSS
1. Fracture
5. Strike (toe)
7. Ogled
8. Strange
9. Abhor
12. Invents
15. Educator
19. Baboon or macaque
21. Stretch
22. The ... of Capri
23. Lofty
24. Naughtiness

DOWN
1. Type of insect
2. Business books review
3. Orchard fruit
4. Engraver
5. Spittle
6. Mooring spots
10. Zone
11. Actor, ... Grant
12. Aggressive dog
13. Resounding noise
14. Confiscated
15. Separate out (wheat)
16. Boxing hold
17. Mummify
18. Me
19. Fulfils (demand)
20. Horse's cry

Crossword 53

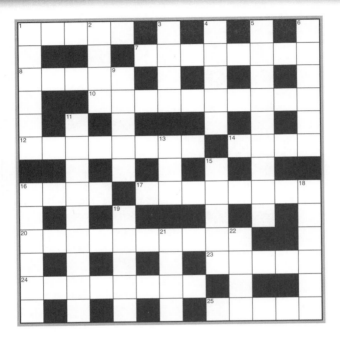

ACROSS
1. Gloomy
7. Make repairs
8. Was the proprietor of
10. Displaces (joint)
12. Aristocrat
14. Slip sideways
16. Ocean predator
17. Pink wading bird
20. Extra costs
23. Immature insect
24. Overshadows
25. Facial hair

DOWN
1. Fractured
2. Filled with wonder
3. Ellipse
4. Cease-fire agreement
5. Participating
6. Shut
9. Plummeted
11. Hazily
13. Entirely
15. Incite to action
16. Unseated
18. Ahead
19. Hews
21. Water grass
22. Auction

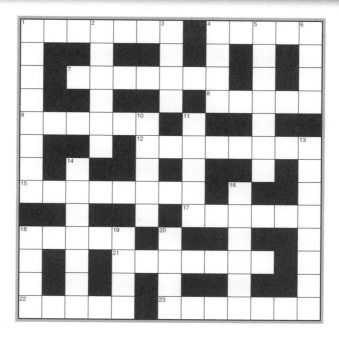

ACROSS
1. True
4. Pituitary or adrenal
7. Stowing space
8. Accurate
9. Me, ... & I
12. Surprised, taken ...
15. Cadets
17. Prohibited narcotic
18. Breakfasts or dinners
21. Climatic conditions
22. Intended
23. Clung (to)

DOWN
1. Most important
2. Captioned
3. Slope
4. Mirth
5. News & current ...
6. Grime
10. Welded
11. Swamp
13. Average
14. Card game
16. Light wind
18. Incapacitate
19. Squash (insect)
20. Festival

Crossword 55

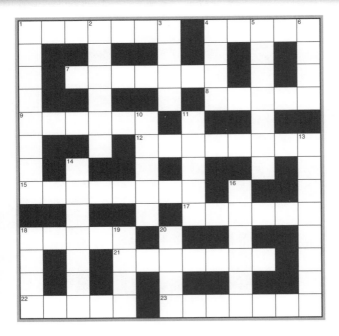

ACROSS
1. As a substitute
4. Picture border
7. Precious stone
8. Use razor
9. Sentries
12. Enthusiasm
15. Models
17. Did business
18. Confident belief
21. Greed
22. Hang
23. Evil action

DOWN
1. Supply with water
2. Stopwatches
3. Pull
4. Short-lived trends
5. Embarrassed
6. Inch (along)
10. Expertise
11. Creature
13. Made unhappy
14. Actress, ... Flockhart
16. Spoiled (of butter)
18. Ward (off)
19. Detest
20. Heat up

ACROSS

1. Connective tissue
5. Tired sigh
7. Brass instrument
8. Pennant mast
9. Parentless child
12. Peruses
15. Common analgesic
19. Together, in ...
21. Bent down
22. Gone away
23. Transmit
24. Banned sports drugs

DOWN

1. Cosmetic fluid
2. Flooded by waves
3. Pixie-like
4. Leaf beverage pourer
5. Barked shrilly
6. Sister's daughters
10. Furtive glance
11. Half-open
12. Solar body
13. Atop
14. Charged atoms
15. Chinese calculating frame
16. Distributed
17. Linear units
18. Joins
19. Excessive
20. Snow shelter

Crossword **57**

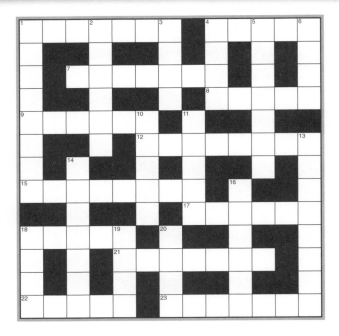

ACROSS
1. Underwent genetic change
4. Less in doubt
7. Ascended (peak)
8. Conscious
9. Montreal is there
12. Be visible once more
15. Sword sheath
17. Moved at easy pace
18. Metallic sound
21. Muslim veil
22. Sneers
23. Herring relative

DOWN
1. Remarkable events
2. Not sinking
3. Confers knighthood on
4. Cleaning agent, caustic ...
5. Despoils
6. Fragrant flower
10. Assortment
11. Black & white mammal
13. Edge of highway
14. Over-zealous supporter
16. Embark, get ...
18. Stuff
19. Fitness clubs
20. Egyptian snakes

Crossword 58

ACROSS

1. Small decorative object
5. Male bovine
7. Garden pool
8. Circling (planet)
9. For each one
12. Guided (to seat)
15. Incapacitate
19. Astute
21. Elaborately
22. Peel (apple)
23. Bridge length
24. Tensions

DOWN

1. Bereaved child
2. Confuse
3. Flee to wed
4. Dining surfaces
5. Combat
6. Myth
10. Freezes, ... over
11. Crustacean with nippers
12. Expend, ... up
13. Tall
14. Trick
15. Wilts
16. Reach
17. Coat collar parts
18. Ruminants' mammary glands
19. More devious
20. Boxing-ring surrounds

Crossword 59

ACROSS
1. Obstructed
5. Door frame post
7. Lively dance
8. Magnificence
9. Halted
12. Ground (teeth)
15. Flower
19. Lightning flash
21. Issue (medication)
22. At a great distance
23. Scan
24. Complete things

DOWN
1. Seize (aircraft)
2. Print media
3. Inflexible
4. Mythical flying reptile
5. Courtroom arbiters
6. Shouldered
10. Highest male singing voice
11. Makes slip-up
12. Precious stone
13. Mother's sister
14. Excessive advertising claim
15. More courageous
16. Dined late
17. Red/yellow shade
18. Dress bottoms
19. Slumbered
20. Cook in oven

ACROSS

1. Agenda topics
7. Remove jockey's seat
8. Speak slowly
10. German cabbage dish
12. Hauling
14. Horse breeding farm
16. Invalid
17. Expanded
20. Musical ensembles
23. Undeveloped insect
24. Graceful style
25. Glide on ice

DOWN

1. Certainly
2. Cuts (grass)
3. The A of AM
4. Levels of command
5. Head start
6. Hired
9. Giggle
11. Bolted (of gate)
13. Religious sister
15. Concerning ships
16. Lasso loops
18. 10-year period
19. Foot lever
21. Diplomat's skill
22. Cloth bag

Crossword **61**

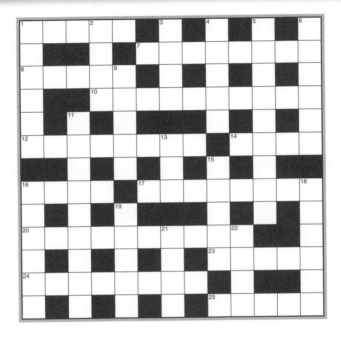

ACROSS
1. Adjust camera lens
7. Relinquish (claim)
8. Produce
10. Children
12. Custodian
14. Ballet, ... *Lake*
16. Canines
17. Devastate
20. Calmly
23. Adolescent
24. Islam or Christianity
25. Glided on snow

DOWN
1. Airborne
2. Unattractive
3. Blood vessel
4. Slightly wet
5. Lingerie
6. Teaching session
9. Not stylish
11. Hilariously
13. Mature
15. Poorly (lit)
16. Expel from country
18. Engraved
19. Pretend
21. Onto
22. Yellow part of egg

ACROSS
1. Inuit canoes
5. Bearded animal
7. Lazy person
8. Temperament
9. Australian gemstone
10. School tests
11. Tends (patients)
13. Detergent foam
14. African wildlife tour
18. Four-door cars
21. Payment for goods
22. Articulated
24. Elude (capture)
25. Beloved
26. Alliance
27. More senior
28. Accustomed (to)
29. Pouted

DOWN
1. Japanese robes
2. South American mountain range
3. Dimensions
4. False names
5. Earned before tax
6. Desert
12. Listening organ
15. Emerges from sleep
16. Stuck (to)
17. Entrails
19. Self-pride
20. Pacified by medication
22. Turns suddenly
23. Incite to action

Crossword **63**

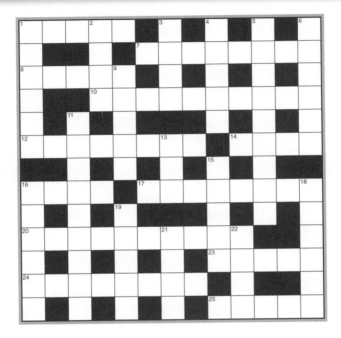

ACROSS
1. Skirt fold
7. Air-filled decorations
8. Out of condition
10. Sixtieth, ..., eightieth
12. Impasse
14. US wild cat
16. Retain
17. Adhesive labels
20. Reconstructing
23. Cut (wood)
24. Itching
25. Magazine copy

DOWN
1. Lopped branches from (tree)
2. Line of rotation
3. Green gemstone
4. Narrow incisions
5. Bonded atom groups
6. Respiratory ailment
9. Recounts
11. Soft-cover book
13. Small bed
15. Symbolic pictures
16. Japanese martial art
18. Polluted mud
19. Long firearm
21. Damp & cold (cave)
22. Spaces (between)

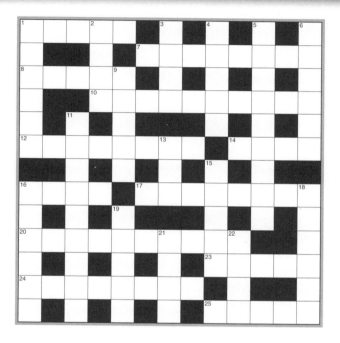

ACROSS
1. Adversary
7. Native American hatchet
8. Shine
10. Character assassination
12. Looking quickly
14. Becomes mature
16. Annual period
17. Blocked from view
20. Exterminated
23. Foxtrot or rumba
24. Increased in depth
25. Troubled

DOWN
1. Fringing
2. Spicy honey liquor
3. Couch
4. Festivities
5. Feigns illness
6. Smelly black & white animals
9. Clemency
11. Computer facts programs
13. Capture (criminal)
15. Performed play
16. Succumbs
18. Shield
19. Mounds
21. Beaten by tennis serve
22. Copenhagen native

Crossword **65**

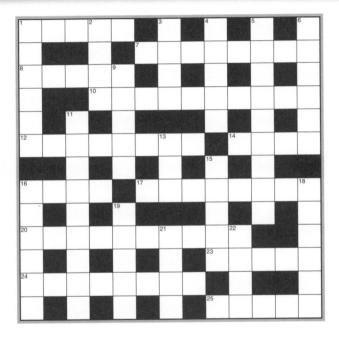

ACROSS
1. Regional
7. Gently
8. Prompt
10. Cleanliness
12. Gripping (tale)
14. Prejudice
16. Tapering fruit
17. Flower sellers
20. Logos
23. Brazilian dance
24. Tidiness
25. Requested, ... for

DOWN
1. Fluid
2. Circle parts
3. Half
4. Perfect
5. Most intelligent
6. Laughing scavengers
9. Covered-in canoe
11. Twin-hulled boat
13. Unwell
15. Arduous hikes
16. Protect (invention)
18. Thread
19. College supervisors
21. In addition
22. Drains

ACROSS

1. Covered-in canoes
5. Spiders' traps
7. Make on loom
8. Pip
9. Musical, My Fair ...
10. Hormone organ
11. Drives forward
13. Freezes, ... over
14. Vehicle depot
18. Absorb (food)
21. Tiny landmass
22. Spiritualist's meeting
24. Wooden post
25. Brave man
26. Bee nest
27. Small insect
28. Present
29. Spiral nails

DOWN

1. Touching with lips
2. Confuse
3. Takes large swallow
4. Pillaged
5. Fusing (metal)
6. Financial estimates
12. Ship's diary
15. Harsh
16. Phenomenal
17. Chores
19. Rage
20. Wavers (on edge)
22. Genders
23. Detest

Crossword 67

ACROSS

1. Cotton strand
5. Wander
7. Elude
8. Company emblem
9. Poodles or terriers
10. Postpone
11. Propels
13. Gorillas or chimpanzees
14. Ballerina
18. Loathe
21. Letters to stars, fan ...
22. Harvested
24. Musical drama
25. ... & queen
26. Become tiresome
27. Nephew's sister
28. Festival
29. Trader

DOWN

1. Added up
2. Grind down
3. Accomplishments
4. Confounded
5. Rewrite
6. Fishermen
12. Tell untruths
15. Greed
16. Scent, eau de ...
17. Venerates
19. Before (poetic)
20. Young child
22. Shouted, ranted & ...
23. First Greek letter

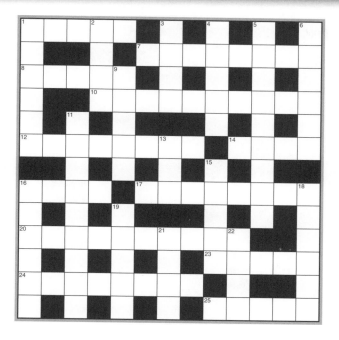

ACROSS

1. Small insect
7. Game fowl
8. Gripe pain
10. At a stalemate
12. Gripping (tale)
14. Three-piece group
16. Prods sharply
17. Imaginary
20. Strategically
23. Adolescent
24. Scored (on par)
25. Yawned open

DOWN

1. Ridiculed
2. Crossword pattern
3. Fitted with horseshoes
4. Beauty shop
5. Retrace footsteps
6. Artist's workplace
9. Fragrant wood
11. Outdoor grills
13. Climbing vine
15. Meekly
16. Jettisoned cargo
18. Secured with rope
19. Fabled giant
21. Beers
22. Hindu meditation

Crossword 69

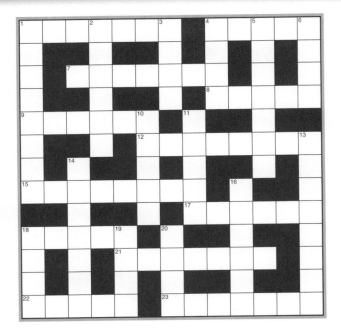

ACROSS
1. Prolonged applause
4. Spongy growths
7. Bathroom fixture
8. Hidden supply
9. Unspoken
12. Be visible once more
15. Christmas season
17. Subtle shade of meaning
18. Shipment of goods
21. Senselessly
22. Waits, ... one's time
23. Please

DOWN
1. Tribute to deceased
2. Little crowns
3. Immature lice
4. Untruths
5. Contradicted
6. Linear unit
10. Exhaust
11. Loaded down
13. Herb
14. Given warning
16. Money case
18. Grooming tool
19. Painting medium
20. Vocalised

ACROSS

1. Dislodge (jockey)
5. Prolonged unconsciousness
7. Animal doctors
8. Flying around (planet)
9. Construes
12. Shellfish
15. Violinist
19. Bite of food
21. Pursed (mouth)
22. Weekly pay
23. Starchy tubers
24. Surround

DOWN

1. Reveal
2. Supermarket lane
3. Entrances
4. Personify
5. Prettiest
6. Cherubs
10. Absconded
11. Throw (dice)
12. The O of SOS
13. Grain store
14. Large deer
15. Droopy
16. Male ducks
17. Appear
18. Arm covering
19. Field hospital worker
20. Oarsman

Crossword 71

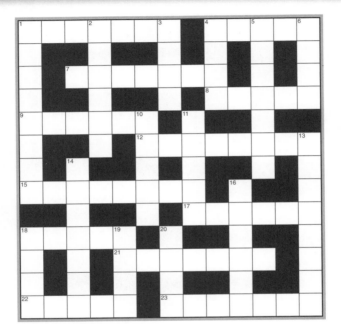

ACROSS
1. Reptiles
4. Alpaca relative
7. Varnish
8. Fill with joy
9. Ebb
12. Scriptwriter's words
15. Most junior
17. Sailing boats
18. Rental agreement
21. National finances
22. Ore veins
23. Worrying needlessly

DOWN
1. Ability to read
2. Eases off
3. Deliberately avoid
4. Traditional wisdom
5. Put in order
6. Attendant
10. Crept along
11. Spiteful
13. Being
14. Sweetened
16. Rascals
18. Quiet interim
19. Slippery fish
20. Animal foot

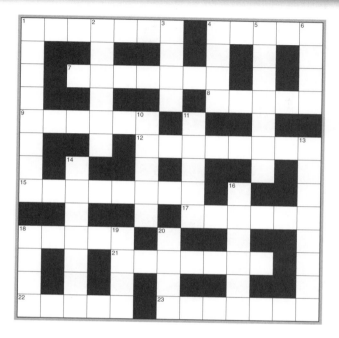

ACROSS

1. Prodding sharply
4. Unsuitable
7. Surgical insert
8. Warning bell
9. Inflammatory skin condition
12. Handbills
15. Negative consequence
17. Radio interference
18. Needing a scratch
21. Greed
22. Remain on feet
23. Young pilchard

DOWN

1. Chattered incoherently
2. Air strike aircraft
3. Cog
4. Minuscule amount
5. Books of maps
6. Pare
10. Also known as
11. Converses
13. Fort
14. Eyelash cosmetic
16. Speared
18. Chills
19. Length unit
20. Wedges forcibly

Crossword 73

ACROSS
1. Person, ... being
7. Game fowl
8. Map within map
10. German cabbage dish
12. Piercing with knife
14. Cut with teeth
16. Be listless
17. Nice
20. Profound
23. Animal trainer
24. Most in want
25. Included

DOWN
1. Hauls up
2. Daunts
3. Clarified butter
4. Face disguises
5. Zealous
6. The ... of Liberty
9. Striped cat
11. Combat aircraft
13. No score
15. Beyond repair
16. Acting wordlessly
18. Journeyed
19. New Zealand birds
21. Talk effusively
22. Cooking fat

Crossword 74

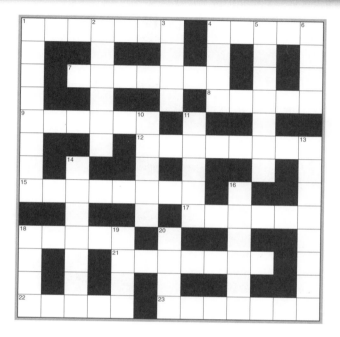

ACROSS

1. Comprehensibly
4. Flimsy
7. Asylum seeker
8. Length of wood
9. Sat lazily
12. Response
15. Came off tracks
17. Strolled
18. Unfasten (garment)
21. With more foliage
22. Necessities
23. Swaying on heels

DOWN

1. Owner of rental property
2. Standards
3. Hindu meditation
4. Sob
5. Demonic
6. Pull with a jerk
10. Dental tool
11. Black & white mammal
13. Aggravating
14. Fine rain
16. Descend rock-face by rope
18. On top of
19. In addition to
20. Set of two

Crossword **75**

ACROSS

1. Deceptive trap
7. Breaks up (group)
8. Innocence excuse
10. Ski resort transport
12. Orderliness
14. Ruptured
16. Cereal husks
17. Compliant
20. Horrific acts of violence
23. Shouted, ranted & ...
24. Ships masters
25. Unfastened

DOWN

1. Mythical flying reptile
2. Globes
3. Scenic outlook
4. Monastery head
5. Poison remedies
6. Rearward (nautical)
9. Foolish
11. Section of writing
13. Underwater vessel
15. Cow mammary gland
16. Go pale
18. Looked after
19. Atlantic or Indian
21. Camp shelter
22. Hewn (logs)

ACROSS

1. Forward
5. Clock face
7. Glowing coal
8. Two-sided contest
9. Knowledge test
10. Paint layers
11. Sound of moving leaves
13. Looks upon
14. Sailing boats
18. Showers
21. Loud noise
22. Customs
24. Snow shelter
25. Departed
26. Tibetan monk
27. Sister's daughter
28. Early harp
29. Rattled

DOWN

1. Neat
2. Allocate
3. Tennis 40/40
4. Gains possession of
5. Kitchen cabinet
6. Police college
12. Illuminated
15. Human body study
16. Sanitation
17. Rebuked
19. Pod vegetable
20. Nourish
22. Family dwellings
23. Model-plane wood

Crossword **77**

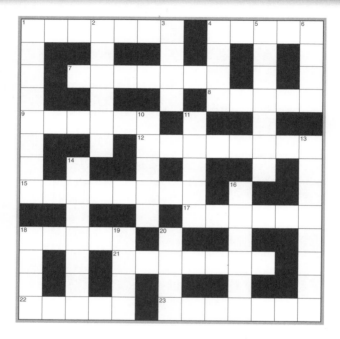

ACROSS
1. Wandering (tribe)
4. Reaffirm (promise)
7. Concerned
8. Complete (crossword)
9. Beat soundly
12. Letter jumbles
15. Taking small bites
17. Radio interference
18. Fashion flair
21. Rubella, German ...
22. End of day
23. Lagged behind

DOWN
1. Last teenage year
2. Smells
3. Trim
4. Metal bars
5. Type of reactor
6. Astute
10. Custom
11. Crime groups
13. Manacled
14. Complying with
16. Profession
18. Read quickly
19. Radiate
20. Log vessel

ACROSS

1. Incinerated
7. Tie or cravat
8. Idiotic (remark)
10. Unselfishly
12. Laid back
14. Dancer, ... Astaire
16. Lash
17. Faithful servant
20. Missile course
23. Sailing boat
24. Regretfully
25. Incidental comment

DOWN

1. Steam generator
2. Religious sisters
3. Coral shipping hazard
4. Heavens
5. Determining dimensions
6. Called (of donkey)
9. Ghostly
11. Set in motion
13. Make last, ... out
15. Loiter
16. Irrigates
18. Shake noisily
19. Premiere
21. Above average height
22. Root vegetables

Crossword **79**

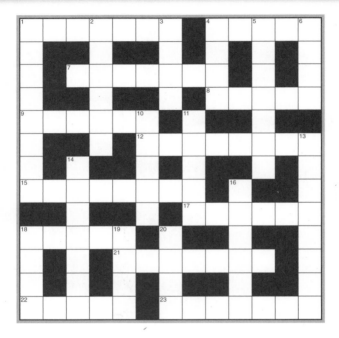

ACROSS
1. Wild
4. Desert wanderer
7. Disbelieving
8. Rent
9. PNG, Papua New ...
12. Identify disease
15. Scriptwriter's words
17. Having raised lines
18. Burn with steam
21. Greed
22. Moisten while roasting
23. Extreme

DOWN
1. Not endorsed
2. Unspecified person
3. Wharf
4. Invalid
5. Spanish bullfighter
6. Springboard descent
10. Wise saying
11. Bread maker
13. Plague
14. Processions
16. Statutes
18. Mortuary stone
19. Stun
20. Set down

ACROSS

1. Inn
5. Creep (towards)
7. Written tests
8. Leer
9. Acceptable
10. Skewered meat
11. Angry crowds
13. Absent
14. Harm
18. Dress ribbons
21. Brass instrument
22. Stood on hind legs
24. Public square
25. Canvas dwelling
26. Despicable
27. Do well (at)
28. Tinted
29. Non-liquids

DOWN

1. Fitted with cogs
2. Edit (text)
3. Slender bottle tops
4. Hare relatives
5. Pressure lines on map
6. False pretence
12. Unborn chick
15. Sharply
16. Changed suitably
17. Improve
19. Beer
20. Makes unhappy
22. Train tracks
23. Blacksmith's block

Crossword 81

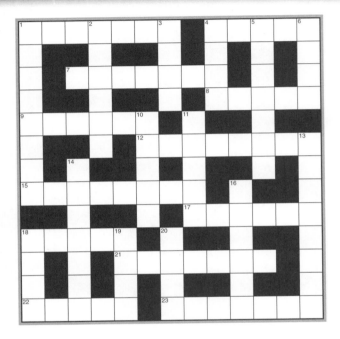

ACROSS

1. Foot arches
4. Grime
7. Reject
8. Clay-based rock
9. Craven person
12. Rain shield
15. Hearing impairment
17. First-born
18. Frantic
21. Responded to stimulus
22. Entitle
23. Leasing

DOWN

1. Charged with crime
2. Of family group
3. Remain
4. Trends
5. Licitly
6. Wish
10. Beach formations
11. Shout insults at
13. Aiding (felon)
14. Sore
16. Most peculiar
18. Leonardo da Vinci's ... Lisa
19. Black bird
20. Animal den

ACROSS
1. Moves ahead
5. Uterus
7. Clip
8. Spanish dance style
9. Woven materials
12. Halting
15. Cash settlement
19. Small packet
21. Obvious
22. Opposite of west
23. Shadow-box
24. Wisps (of smoke)

DOWN
1. Escapades
2. Allow entry to
3. Informal eateries
4. Rarely encountered
5. Sunken ships
6. Displeased jeering
10. Solely
11. Residence
12. Severed
13. Greenish-blue
14. Mosquito bite irritation
15. Pressed fabric folds
16. Hair of angora goat
17. Most recent
18. The United ... of America
19. Glossy silk
20. Shout for joy

Crossword **83**

ACROSS
1. Mobile homes
5. Clock sound
7. US space agency
8. Public at large
9. Strikingly unusual
12. More cluttered
15. Roman XVI
19. Religious lecture
21. Ravager
22. Fish-landing pole
23. Extinct bird
24. Dwindled

DOWN
1. Kayaks
2. Separately
3. Meat jelly
4. Lithe
5. Long claws
6. Zoo custodian
10. Type of marble
11. Not in use
12. Human male
13. Underside of shoe
14. Article
15. Appeared to be
16. Red salad fruit
17. Evaded (capture)
18. Wounded by blade
19. Leather strip
20. Scoundrel

ACROSS
1. Havoc
7. Beekeeper
8. Vocal sound
10. Manual art
12. Elegant
14. Honey drink
16. Boast
17. Undo
20. Available
23. Recorded (music)
24. Hugging
25. Used keyboard

DOWN
1. Exploring caverns
2. Exclamation of pain
3. Mimicked
4. Receive ball
5. Thin wires
6. Declared
9. Roof overhangs
11. Procession
13. Grecian vase
15. Gymnastics event
16. Tree limb
18. Required
19. Bible song
21. Taverns
22. Simple

Crossword **85**

ACROSS
1. Long trip
5. High tennis deliveries
7. Cast a line
8. Not one
9. Two-sided contest
10. Scraping by, ... out a living
11. Lessened
13. Opposite of west
14. Model for public ridicule
18. Stop
21. Social bigot
22. Senselessness
24. Lazy person
25. Bang (toe)
26. Advertising symbol
27. Opt
28. Corrosive liquid
29. Lengthen

DOWN
1. Antique (car)
2. Vigilant
3. Alleviated
4. Lit
5. Accounts books
6. Sanctifies
12. Poultry product
15. Extremist
16. Partook of liquor
17. Succumbed
19. Culminate
20. Neck gland
22. Furious
23. Bay

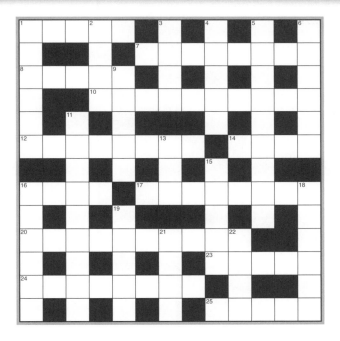

ACROSS

1. South American parrot
7. Bestride
8. Tennis 40/40
10. Ambling
12. Taking (revenge)
14. Bee nest
16. Australian gemstone
17. Wickedly enjoyable
20. Meteorologists
23. Of sound
24. Furthest back
25. Unfasten (garment)

DOWN

1. Interfere
2. Curves
3. Daze
4. Strong winds
5. Supplements in food
6. Small hound
9. Third planet
11. Twin-hulled boat
13. Formerly named
15. Rants
16. Ahead
18. Safety boot's reinforcement
19. Hand digit
21. Pink (complexion)
22. Midday

Crossword **87**

ACROSS
1. Massaging
5. Multiple-birth child
7. Canned fish
8. Nonprofessionals
9. Detest
12. Tribal leader
15. Pastures
19. Tendons
21. More humane
22. Courageous
23. Small, soft feathers
24. Admires

DOWN
1. Water boiler
2. Modify
3. Angry
4. Brief look
5. Waited in line
6. Refuse to acknowledge
10. Charismatic air
11. Brave man
12. Belonging to him
13. Opposed to
14. Fashion
15. Disguised
16. Benumb
17. More cautious
18. Incidental comments
19. Varieties
20. Aristocratic

ACROSS
1. First Greek letter
7. Rasping
8. Auctioneer's hammer
10. Obedience
12. Insulin-deficient person
14. Frees
16. Poodles or terriers
17. Unmerited
20. Forgivable
23. Skin-diving gear
24. Beer steins
25. Assigned specific area

DOWN
1. Used fishing rod
2. Weeding implements
3. Fraud
4. Untrue
5. Separations into parts
6. Stars' business managers
9. Baits
11. Type of citrus fruit
13. Pub
15. Doesn't succeed
16. Warehouses
18. Forceful request
19. Reef growth
21. Lends a hand to
22. Resound

Crossword 89

ACROSS

1. Spanish fleet
5. Unfortunately
7. Haul strenuously
8. Paint roughly
9. Peruse
10. Elsewhere excuse
11. Choked with sweetness
13. Not here
14. African wildlife tour
18. Readjusts (clock)
21. Sore crust
22. Carried out orders
24. Unsuitable
25. Pottery oven
26. Clear (weather)
27. Unhealthily overweight
28. Grows old
29. Continues (subscription)

DOWN

1. Kidnaps
2. London's Westminster ...
3. In front
4. Seafarer
5. Antennas
6. Insistent
12. Hearing organ
15. Curving
16. Pure white animals
17. Spiked
19. Recede
20. Makes unhappy
22. River mammal
23. Pixie-like

ACROSS

1. Survives longer than
5. Hawaiian dance
7. Attire
8. Circling
9. Expels from homeland
12. Fatigued
15. Give back
19. Diamond-cuts
21. Without shoes
22. Linear unit
23. Aromatic herb
24. Reading disorder

DOWN

1. Wild sprees
2. Written defamation
3. Apertures
4. Pacify
5. More heated
6. Used fishing rod
10. Charged particles
11. Reverberate
12. Misfortune
13. Singer's solo
14. Tiny landmass
15. Synagogue scholars
16. Illegally take
17. Refill rifle
18. Respiratory ailment
19. Destinies
20. Bell sound

Crossword 91

ACROSS
1. Promising
5. Fleshy part of ear
7. Musical drama
8. Remove
9. Bell-shaped fruit
10. Precise
11. Rampaged
13. Is obliged to pay
14. Tell
18. Stop
21. Inquires
22. Set alight
24. Dark
25. Knitting stitch
26. Treaty
27. Eighth, ninth, ...
28. Wagers
29. Barked in pain

DOWN
1. Former soldier
2. Immobile
3. Injured with horns
4. Conveyed (message)
5. Portable computers
6. Dam-building
   creatures
12. Sprite
15. Unclear
16. Disparaging remarks
17. Shouting
19. Poultry product
20. Gave therapy to
22. Irritating to the skin
23. Kathmandu is there

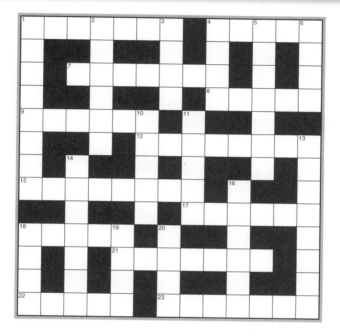

ACROSS

1. Foyers
4. Act of foolishness
7. Aircraft attendant
8. Mops (deck)
9. Tile-chip picture
12. Refugees
15. Stalkers
17. Degraded
18. Public square
21. Ringing (of bell)
22. Stage of development
23. Crossing (river)

DOWN

1. Connective tissue
2. Be disloyal to
3. Yacht pole
4. Short-lived trends
5. Situated
6. Tropical root vegetables
10. Surrendered
11. Light timber
13. Pacifying
14. Mosquito-borne fever
16. Showered
18. Inflate, ... up
19. Land measure
20. Petty quarrel

Crossword 93

ACROSS
1. Keep score
7. Kitchen strainer
8. Son or daughter
10. Woven artworks
12. Revolving
14. Young deer
16. Respectfully, on bended ...
17. Like an emblem
20. Gallant
23. Try out (food)
24. Occupying
25. Fire (at) from cover

DOWN
1. Ploy
2. Jaunty voice rhythm
3. Tedious person
4. Impetuous
5. To be recommended
6. Cropped up
9. Dawdle
11. Pre-mission sessions
13. Negative vote
15. Regarding
16. Struck with foot
18. Cheddar or Edam
19. Dog's skin disease
21. Sprints
22. Cut (timber)

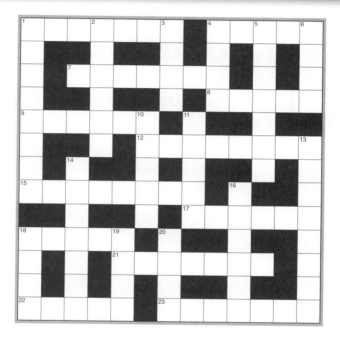

ACROSS
1. Disclose
4. Precise
7. Volunteered
8. Hot water burn
9. Lump of food
12. Reproduce (2-6)
15. Cattle charge
17. Riches
18. Start of era

21. Disturbed
22. Frightening
23. Tough meat tissue

DOWN
1. Gradually diminishes
2. Open out
3. Merit
4. Terminates
5. Yearbook
6. Informed

10. Snooped
11. Wood fastener
13. Place as monarch
14. Portable rocket-launcher
16. Wage recipients
18. Hearing organs
19. Not clearly defined
20. Warbled

Crossword **95**

ACROSS
1. One million watts
5. Shapeless mass
7. Magician's rod
8. Fruit groves
9. Kindest
12. World statesmen
15. Spread out
19. Made amends
21. Kings or queens
22. Rip
23. Recess
24. Quickly drew

DOWN
1. Cutting (grass)
2. Confuse
3. Abandon (mission)
4. Itch
5. Reduced car speed
6. Managers
10. Hair spiral
11. Desex
12. Pot top
13. Father's sister
14. Smooth
15. Flower part
16. Assail
17. Votes into office
18. Greatly loved
19. Supermarket lane
20. Of the eyes

ACROSS
1. Fracture
5. Scream
7. Incendiary device
8. Ambled
9. Build up
12. Fought rowdily
15. Cooks in juices
19. Martial art
21. Whitened
22. Metropolis
23. Long narrative
24. Shame

DOWN
1. North American feline
2. Fossil resin
3. Supermarket lane
4. Spookier
5. Rainbow hue
6. Wedged
10. Unconscious state
11. Large jars
12. Public transport
13. Opera song
14. Volcanic matter
15. Financial inducements
16. Galapagos lizard
17. Engraved
18. Rewrite on machine
19. Prestige
20. Crop up again

Crossword 97

ACROSS
1. Increase in intensity
5. Post of doorway
7. Provoke
8. Undo (belt)
9. Acquired skill
12. Detested
15. Most expensive
19. Proverbs
21. Dig
22. Hawaiian dance
23. Invalid
24. Drench

DOWN
1. Inundate
2. Viper
3. Fully-grown
4. Plant seed part
5. Book cover
6. Made (beer)
10. Charismatic air
11. Identify
12. Ignited
13. Among
14. Dangled
15. Lower dignity of
16. Recollect
17. Smudges
18. Large property
19. Vigilant
20. Hate

ACROSS

1. Ventured (guess)
5. Small measure of spirits
7. Hunger pain
8. Sword holder
9. Close
12. Holds tenderly
15. Male rower
19. Legendary
21. Hidden (motive)
22. Motorist's fury, road ...
23. Oxen harness
24. Defames

DOWN

1. Wishing
2. Hostility
3. Coated in fine dirt
4. Fabrics dealer
5. Added soundtrack to
6. Gnat-like flies
10. Slightly open
11. Hat edge
12. Is able to
13. Distinctive air
14. Brief calm
15. Reside in
16. Restful
17. Dodges
18. Vipers
19. Land, terra ...
20. Drilled hole

Crossword 99

ACROSS
1. Drive forward
5. Needle pricks
7. Musical, The Phantom Of The ...
8. Rip violently
9. Genuine
10. Belonging to them
11. Treatment
13. Printing fluids
14. Regatta entrants
18. Vital body parts
21. Protracted
22. Introduced to solid food
24. Haul strenuously
25. Store (cargo)
26. Precipitation
27. Short-circuited
28. Extremely
29. Crude huts

DOWN
1. Depict
2. Chaplain
3. Tall
4. Souvenir
5. Jolting
6. Darken
12. Small spot
15. Follower
16. Major road
17. Superficial cut
19. Regret
20. Railway shunting tracks
22. Unwanted plants
23. Great artery

Crossword **100**

ACROSS

1. Proffered
5. Jest
7. A long time
8. Remarkable events
9. Refreshment stands
12. Pursued stealthily
15. Bewildered
19. Sponged
21. Swiftest
22. Open mouth wide
23. Poultry products
24. Calming drug

DOWN

1. Appreciation
2. Brushes (off)
3. Cavorts
4. Straight
5. Wild African canine
6. Eventuated
10. Was obliged to pay
11. Ship's spine
12. Lump of turf
13. Water
14. Door handle
15. Muslim temple
16. Dance nightclubs
17. Painters' tripods
18. Stick (to)
19. Loved excessively,
    ... on
20. Prejudiced person

Crossword **101**

ACROSS
1. Keeps steady
5. Ballet skirt
7. Windmill arm
8. Looking sideways
9. Flower syrup
12. Rebuking
15. Proxy
19. Cherubs
21. Widens
22. Roman garment
23. Jealousy
24. Skilled performers

DOWN
1. Of cattle
2. Turn away
3. Large roll of tobacco
4. Stiffen (fabric)
5. Zigzagged (of yacht)
6. Encouraging
10. Placid
11. Similar
12. Snooker stick
13. Ferrous metal
14. Small island
15. Agile
16. Notoriety
17. Skin disorder
18. Compositions
19. Resource
20. Fence openings

ACROSS
1. Swallowing fluid
5. Handle
7. Snout
8. Exciting
9. Voice box
12. Medieval farm worker
15. Subdued (riot)
19. Straighten
21. Beaten
22. River barrier
23. Fruit pip
24. Made stable

DOWN
1. Swing from a rope
2. In want
3. Alphabetical listing
4. Sideways look
5. Australian marsupials
6. Pail
10. Rampant
11. Invalid
12. Helicopter landing area
13. Similar
14. Feel pain
15. Officially allotted amounts
16. Iguana or monitor
17. Imprints (on mind)
18. Loved deeply
19. Unwarranted
20. Curtsied

Crossword **103**

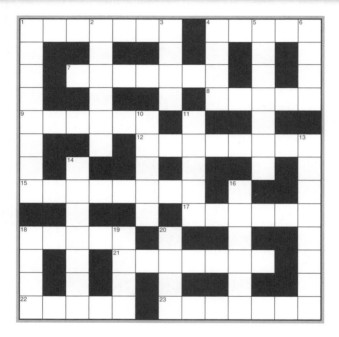

ACROSS
1. Forceful
4. Shirtsleeve edges
7. Cats
8. Stockpile
9. Accommodated
12. Occasion
15. Release
17. Laundry stiffener
18. Assisted

21. Citrus crop
22. Cherub
23. Tied (laces)

DOWN
1. Away from summit
2. Opposed
3. Sugar source
4. Money
5. Scavenges

6. Beach material
10. Female opera singers
11. Dull pains
13. Hitched
14. Tolerating
16. Lying dormant
18. Spiritual glow
19. Girl's plaything
20. Songbird

ACROSS

1. Particular
5. Very dry
7. Premonition
8. Shivers with disgust
9. Gleaming
12. US frontier movie
15. Bumped in crowd
19. Wax pencil
21. Tolerable
22. Ardent
23. Antlered animal
24. Broad open areas

DOWN

1. Absorbent cloth
2. Pine fruits
3. Questionable
4. Direction of travel
5. Prescription medicines abuser
6. Blueprint
10. Is in debt to
11. Yacht's canvas
12. Marry
13. Fly high
14. Glimpse
15. Poked abruptly
16. Horror
17. Fit for consumption
18. Charged electrodes
19. Economical
20. Once more

Crossword **105**

ACROSS
1. Peruvian mammal
7. Tactic
8. Flower segment
10. Longest
12. Muffled
14. Percussion instrument
16. Untruths
17. Had an impact on
20. People in books
23. More recent
24. Battlefield ditches
25. Abundant

DOWN
1. Pruned
2. Dinner or lunch
3. Doe's mate
4. Wood-turning machine
5. Rejoice
6. Method
9. Flood barrier
11. Tears (skin) jaggedly
13. Folklore creature
15. Crave, ... for
16. Find
18. Graduate's award
19. Cattle farm
21. Drew
22. Coal vein

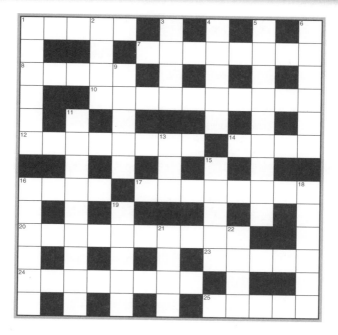

ACROSS

1. Rapid
7. Likely
8. Trample
10. Jingling percussion instrument
12. Relieve of anxieties
14. Piebald
16. Young lions
17. Hand-clapping
20. Pirates
23. Italian dish
24. Personal reminiscence
25. Rap

DOWN

1. Artist's model
2. Brave deed
3. Infant's bed
4. Concerning
5. Unaware
6. Decapitate
9. Common flower
11. Cooked outdoors
13. Dangerous sea current
15. Suck noisily
16. Venomous hooded snakes
18. Set off
19. Comes to earth
21. Feeds on
22. Hewn (logs)

Crossword 107

ACROSS
1. Rot
7. Forbid
8. Notions
10. Children
12. Pamphlets
14. Curves over
16. Sleeve edge
17. Exterior
20. Standing down as monarch
23. In front
24. Homicides
25. Commenced

DOWN
1. Nonsense
2. Not here
3. Signal
4. Austere
5. Technical drawing
6. Distorts
9. Spiritual beings
11. Yellow bulb flowers
13. Levy
15. Red dye
16. Cantankerous
18. Dull & overcast (sky)
19. Pungent
21. Labels
22. Clarified butter

ACROSS
1. Wax taper
5. Bird's bill
7. Relating to speech
8. Hurried
9. Henhouse produce
10. Gorge
11. Dormant
13. In a casual way
14. Weekly earnings
18. Orb
21. Stylish
22. Abided by (rules)
24. Moral principle
25. King cat
26. Prod
27. Male duck
28. Rock band's sound boosters
29. Chatted

DOWN
1. Monarch's residences
2. Sidestep
3. Oust from property
4. Scratches (surface)
5. Imperfection
6. Sharp-cornered
12. And not
15. Religious non-belief
16. Rises
17. Eastern veil
19. Hotel
20. Lasted
22. Eight singers
23. Artist's stand

Crossword 109

ACROSS
1. Fruit extract
7. Army rank
8. Small ships
10. Renowned performers
12. Exciting
14. Brass instrument
16. Travel by sea
17. Retrieves
20. People in book
23. Annual periods
24. Editing (text)
25. Lodge firmly

DOWN
1. Prodded
2. Infants' beds
3. Stirred from sleep
4. Muscle cramp
5. Prized
6. Blood component
9. Sweetener
11. Steered (course)
13. Wrath
15. Feel anxious
16. Used drinking straw
18. Pickled
19. Printed greetings
21. Heavy weights
22. Fabric join

ACROSS

1. Royal residence
5. Single article
7. Slow speaking style
8. Immigration permit
9. Lose fluid
10. Track down
11. Drives back
13. Win
14. Sighed sleepily
18. Handing (out)
21. Greek liquor
22. Ten, ..., twelve
24. Indulge in reverie
25. Legacy document
26. Seep
27. Bird of prey
28. Chops
29. Laundry machines

DOWN

1. Lack of money
2. Humble (oneself)
3. Reworks (text)
4. Marched in procession
5. Illicit
6. Underhand avoidance
12. Untrue statement
15. Insulting
16. Asian ribbon food
17. Branch off
19. Petroleum product
20. Goslings' dads
22. Lodge firmly
23. Hard black wood

Crossword 111

ACROSS
1. Prank
5. Upon
7. Stare lustfully at
8. Narrowed eyes
9. Amalgamates
12. Put in quarantine
15. Blood relationship
19. Fixed (price)
21. Supplies funds for
22. Stirred from sleep
23. Eat
24. Nice

DOWN
1. Mass departure
2. Talented
3. Donkeys
4. Oozes
5. Yearly
6. Oar
10. Religious statue
11. Every single
12. Mischievous sprite
13. Woodwind instrument
14. Keenly excited
15. Wounded by blade
16. Ferocious
17. Polar covering
18. Strangest
19. Glue
20. Formal dresses

ACROSS

1. Desert illusion
5. Wound with dagger
7. Adjudicator
8. Confiscate
9. Male fowl
10. Seat
11. Shocked
13. Give off
14. Decrees
18. Lessening
21. Tinted
22. Colloquial sayings
24. Protect
25. Foundation
26. Travel cost
27. Shelf
28. Belonging to
   that girl
29. Ambulance warnings

DOWN

1. Natural gas
2. Sports ground
3. Oust
4. Move forward
5. Confidential matters
6. Sale by bids
12. Perched
15. Eddie Murphy comedy,
   Daddy ... (3,3)
16. Truncheons
17. Threads
19. As well
20. Sealants
22. Lazes
23. Deduce

Crossword 113

ACROSS
1. Red salad fruit
5. Chilly
7. Substantial
8. Formerly
9. Clothed
10. Fish commercially
11. Shows way
13. Painting medium
14. Bicycle for two
18. Representatives
21. Imitated
22. Subtle shade of meaning
24. Hang loosely
25. Challenge
26. Fiji's capital
27. Beat faster (of heart)
28. Ill at ease
29. Transgressed

DOWN
1. Pondered
2. Edit
3. Skips
4. Mosquito-borne fever
5. Violent tropical storm
6. Printed handout
12. Ram's mate
15. Clap
16. Frail with age
17. Patterns of small pieces
19. African antelope
20. Flight attendant
22. Has (to)
23. Malicious fire-setting

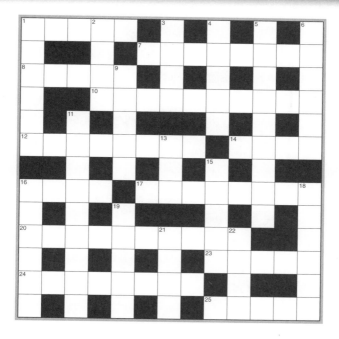

ACROSS
1. Prevent entry of
7. Grainy polishing substance
8. Owl calls
10. German cabbage dish
12. Meat plant
14. Ancestry, family ...
16. Waterside loading platform
17. Obvious
20. Overstate
23. Alleviated
24. Astronauts
25. Rise to feet

DOWN
1. Mexican flower
2. Performs on stage
3. Competent
4. Is deficient in
5. Did not concur
6. Soft
9. Briny
11. Twin-hulled vessel
13. Mischievous sprite
15. Squander
16. Nauseated
18. Nursed
19. White wading bird
21. Regrets
22. North, south, ..., west

Crossword 115

ACROSS
1. Abodes on wheels
5. Headwear
7. Uncluttered
8. Insulin-deficient person
9. South American cloak
12. Tussle
15. Suppressed (riot)
19. Secondary route
21. Authenticity
22. Spiritual glow
23. Split apart
24. Uncommon items

DOWN
1. Parachute part
2. Ancient Mexican
3. Of sound
4. Less fresh
5. African 'laughing' scavengers
6. Safe
10. Brief letter
11. Ship's frame
12. Money roll
13. Simple
14. Filled tortilla
15. Tremble
16. Taxed
17. More nervous
18. Principles
19. Purchaser
20. Bake in oven

ACROSS

1. Overdue (bill)
5. Tree part
7. Hostile opponent
8. Crustacean with nippers
9. Captures (criminal)
10. Uniform
11. Accessories
13. Wig material
14. Disorderly crowd
18. Quit
21. Heavily promote
22. Held responsible
24. Illustrious
25. Discover
26. Delivery vehicles
27. Wear away
28. Act
29. Long claws

DOWN

1. Obscure
2. Fossil resin
3. Concave impressions
4. Wander
5. Hangs unlawfully
6. Walking slowly
12. Trouble
15. Whenever
16. Mixed
17. Arch over eye
19. Snake-like fish
20. Naturists
22. Besieged
23. Blacksmith's block

Crossword 117

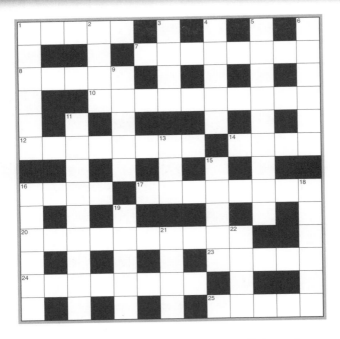

ACROSS
1. Person, ... being
7. Beautified
8. Potter's turning device
10. Most disobedient
12. Rekindle
14. Finance
16. Steals from
17. Wide Mexican hat
20. Pop instrumentalists
23. Urbane
24. Vibrated
25. Roamed

DOWN
1. New World's ... monkey
2. Prayer ending
3. Catch (stocking)
4. Sections
5. Timetabled
6. Reworked (text)
9. Tibetan monks
11. Partly cooked
13. Self-pride
15. Touches at one end
16. Entitlements
18. Break the law
19. Smears
21. Chilled
22. Japanese-style wrestling

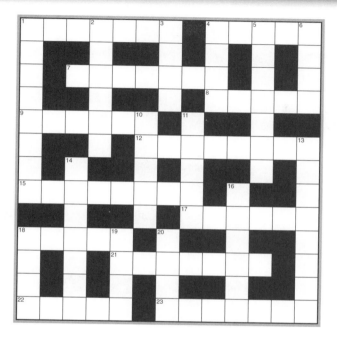

ACROSS
1. Boat race meeting
4. Shine (at)
7. Ineffective
8. Wear away
9. Be present
12. Mentally conjured up
15. Surgeons' knives
17. Warmed up
18. Diamond-cut

21. Pulling with a jerk
22. Depart
23. Green gem

DOWN
1. Sets free
2. Corridors
3. Top pilots
4. Otherwise, or ...
5. Perfume

6. Loll
10. Restaurant patron
11. Drastic
13. Muffled
14. Eyelash cosmetic
16. Cloth sign
18. Drop
19. Write with keyboard
20. Largest body joint

Crossword 119

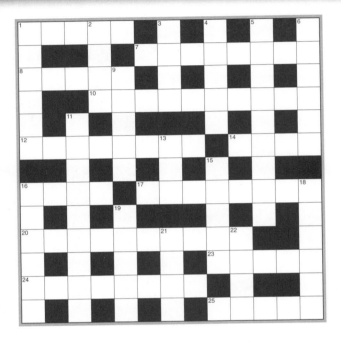

ACROSS
1. Haughty
7. Implicates
8. Senseless (comment)
10. Half-circumference
12. Practical people
14. Dog's feet
16. Jealousy
17. Military occupiers
20. Firming (grip)
23. Subjugated
24. Curled hair locks
25. Roof end

DOWN
1. First paint coat
2. Decorative garden pots
3. Against
4. Actor, ... Williams
5. Withdrew to safe place
6. Escorts
9. Strange
11. Saving from wreck
13. Metal in bronze
15. Visit as ghost
16. Carnivores, meat ...
18. Ice-cream dessert
19. Circular reef
21. Pecans or almonds
22. Festival

ACROSS
1. Puzzle
5. Wharf
7. Spree
8. Inheritor
9. Bread portion
10. Not explicit
11. Film star dog
13. Serving platter
14. Join in half-heartedly
18. Ran rapidly
21. Printing fluids
22. Afraid
24. Remove completely
25. Grant
26. Injure with horns
27. Recurrent period
28. Legend
29. Torrid

DOWN
1. Expelled air
2. Disease agents
3. Higher than
4. Caught on barb
5. Crosses out
6. Mime
12. Sick
15. Yearly stipend
16. Implore
17. Increase in attractiveness
19. Rainbow shape
20. Frail with age
22. Genders
23. Debate

Crossword 121

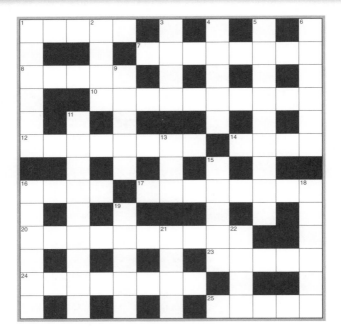

ACROSS

1. Coral barriers
7. Looks for
8. Hard skin on toes
10. Private wildlife custodian
12. Interfering people
14. Upper limbs
16. Impulsive thought
17. Motor repairer
20. Blocked
23. Arrives at wharf
24. Lengthen
25. Bring together

DOWN

1. Ethnic bias
2. Large tooth
3. In this place
4. Unmerciful
5. Child's escort
6. Dethrones
9. Marten fur
11. Confession
13. Regret
15. Tear into strips
16. Made from timber
18. Morally pure
19. Pulls heavily
21. Metropolis
22. Not up

ACROSS

1. Wild West tavern
5. Jolt
7. Alpine song
8. Fossil fuel
9. Fleur-de-lis plant
10. Egg shapes
11. Gone on horseback
13. Ballerina's skirt
14. African wildlife tour
18. Small chore
21. Lacking sensation
22. Cable supports
24. Just right
25. Physical hurt
26. Incendiary device
27. Verbal exams
28. Allows to
29. Prime of life

DOWN

1. Fastens
2. Stared lasciviously at
3. Synthetic fabric
4. Move forward
5. Heat bubble
6. Wet slightly
12. Listening organ
15. Flatter to excess
16. Pink-eyed rabbits
17. Against the law
19. Actor, ... Liotta
20. Ignore orders
22. Opulent
23. Hotel foyer

Crossword **123**

ACROSS
1. Singing parts
5. Miserly
7. Ocean mammal
8. Truss
9. Slight quarrel
10. Oily fruit
11. Ascended
13. Globes
14. Meekly
18. Respond
21. Appeal
22. Devious
24. Eighth, ..., tenth
25. Novel thought
26. Formal dance
27. Yonder, over ...
28. Verge
29. Close relatives

DOWN
1. Full of energy
2. Assistants
3. Faint
4. SW African republic
5. Small celestial bodies
6. Genial
12. Conger or moray
15. Subtly referred
16. Issue (from)
17. Not as old
19. Neither
20. Sovereignty
22. Principal
23. Stamp book

ACROSS
1. Swellings
7. Interim
8. Perfect
10. Woven wall-hangings
12. Arriving at
14. Sweetly appealing
16. Spoilt child
17. Orators
20. Senselessly
23. Abated
24. Languidness
25. Cranium

DOWN
1. Dally
2. Fire fuel
3. Festival
4. Bring together
5. Made fun of
6. Leaseholder
9. Wood-shaping machine
11. Small parrots
13. Crab's pinch
15. Aesop tale
16. Wrist ornament
18. Summer shoe
19. Have buoyancy
21. Wise person
22. Tug sharply

Crossword 125

ACROSS
1. Tile-chip design
5. In between
7. Domain
8. Class-conscious person
9. Speak to God
10. Of the ear
11. Cadence
13. Curved-bill wading bird
14. Tugged sharply
18. Coyest
21. Dry (of champagne)
22. Rang
24. Royal headwear
25. Object of worship
26. Destroy
27. Tribal senior
28. Dedicatory poems
29. Spanks

DOWN
1. Niggardly
2. Monastery superior
3. Top of milk
4. Nursing directors
5. Boost (sound)
6. Sloped writing style
12. Garden tool
15. Worn by friction
16. Water boilers
17. Insists on
19. Shade
20. Latest information
22. Couples
23. Main artery

ACROSS

1. Consecrate with oil
5. Cut (grass)
7. Black wood
8. Opera solo
9. Did breaststroke
10. Circle (planet)
11. Examiner
13. Supplements, ... out
14. Plunder
18. Coyest
21. Petty quarrel
22. Go back on deal
24. Consumption
25. Be unsuccessful
26. Sound boosters
27. Tied (shoes)
28. Catch sight of
29. Dress ribbons

DOWN

1. Electric socket converter
2. Unsuitable
3. Male voice
4. Recreational activities
5. Suspense novel
6. Loom operators
12. Poultry product
15. Zoo inmates
16. Appallingly
17. Beautify
19. Shade
20. Locks of hair
22. Splits apart
23. Comes closer to

Crossword 127

ACROSS
1. Body part
7. Most unassuming
8. Supporting beam
10. Spearing (whale)
12. Male astronaut
14. Thoroughfare
16. Seaside crustacean
17. Leave hotel (5,3)
20. Vulnerable spots
23. Desk
24. Move
25. Carved into shape

DOWN
1. Planets' paths
2. Bridge span
3. Zodiac crossover
4. Monastery head
5. Punctuation mark
6. Presented (play)
9. Alleviates
11. Pleasant tasting
13. Volcanic debris
15. Eight-piece group
16. Cringes
18. Sewing cotton
19. Bring into force
21. Location
22. Fully satisfy

Crossword 128

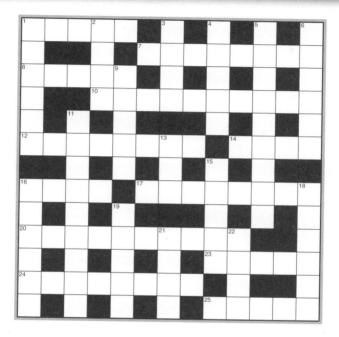

ACROSS
1. Large jet plane
7. Fleece clippers
8. Twist (nose)
10. Hot season
12. Tactful person
14. Mutilate
16. Gave temporarily
17. Salvage
20. Uncultivated region
23. Mayhem
24. Land use entitlement
25. Devout

DOWN
1. Protruded
2. Foundation garments
3. Fake
4. Carnivals
5. Pledges
6. High regard
9. Personal glory
11. Lacking backbone
13. Gorilla or chimpanzee
15. Collision
16. Solicitor
18. Casts out
19. Fabric joins
21. No part
22. Indian dress

Crossword 129

ACROSS
1. 3-sided object
5. Not swift
7. Abstain from food
8. Undid (trousers)
9. Executes (law)
12. Portable steps
15. Mocking
19. That is to say
21. Infancy
22. Roman gown
23. Be brave enough
24. Makes stable

DOWN
1. Chewy confectionery
2. Loft
3. Beetle larvae
4. Form of dermatitis
5. Drained
6. Thick slices
10. Church recess
11. Travel along runway
12. Lower limb
13. Computer input
14. Relieve
15. Prodded sharply
16. Rewrite on keyboard
17. Synthetic fabrics
18. Detour
19. Light push
20. Reduced volume of

ACROSS
1. Troubled state
5. Diplomacy
7. Delete
8. Desperate (circumstances)
9. Ensnare
10. Discord
11. Move spasmodically
13. Swirl
14. Raw vegetable dishes
18. Miserable
21. Palm cereal
22. Meat spit
24. Stretch (for)
25. New Zealand bird
26. Hyphen
27. Push
28. Excited
29. Arrived (of day)

DOWN
1. Makes current
2. Upright
3. Instruct
4. Dealt with
5. Ties up
6. Supermodel, ... Schiffer
12. Atlantic fish
15. Astounding
16. Greatly loving
17. Maroons
19. Irritate
20. Swayed suddenly
22. Drew back (in fear)
23. Bequeath

Crossword 131

ACROSS
1. Went aboard ship
5. Had to repay
7. On an occasion
8. Tidiness
9. Greatly pleases
12. Makes beloved
15. Temper outburst
19. Did penance (for)
21. Living being
22. Woodwind instrument
23. Tropical tuber
24. Goes back over (path)

DOWN
1. Summoned up
2. Skilled
3. Monarchs
4. Fire-breathing monster
5. Elaborately embellished
6. Dance clubs
10. Nameless author
11. At all times
12. Deciduous tree
13. Soil
14. Yemen port
15. Gullet
16. Red salad fruit
17. Less attractive
18. Ruminants' mammary glands
19. Let in
20. Atmosphere layer

ACROSS
1. Living entity
5. Minuscule amount
7. Company symbol
8. Expresses excitement (over)
9. Shows gratitude to
12. Tampered
15. Retaliated for
19. Fused
21. Inhibit
22. Object of worship
23. Toboggan
24. Models of virtue

DOWN
1. Wise bird's chicks
2. Oak kernel
3. Objects
4. Intention
5. Accustomed
6. Ridiculous
10. Unit of land
11. Male monarch
12. Wet soil
13. Deceive
14. Tolkien's The ... Of The Rings
15. Burglar deterrents
16. Snared
17. Pitch tent
18. Confuses
19. Underground worker
20. Telling untruths

Crossword **133**

ACROSS
1. Exposed film
5. Front of ship
7. Opposed to
8. Medieval farm workers
9. But
12. Public speakers
15. Overlook
19. Sulked
21. Gave cards wrongly
22. Feel angry
23. Noisy
24. Meeting plan

DOWN
1. More orderly
2. In existence
3. Data supplied
4. Income cheat, tax ...
5. Oil source
6. Cleanses
10. Block (up)
11. Skin aperture
12. Cereal grass
13. Female voice
14. Unseat from power
15. Common
16. Came to shore
17. Man-made waterways
18. Cling (to)
19. Eye cover
20. Not given food

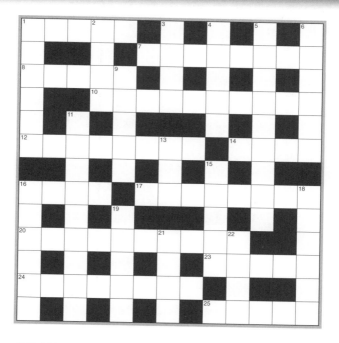

ACROSS
1. Atlantic or Pacific
7. Soldiers' quarters
8. Praise
10. Sealed against moisture
12. Watering down
14. Pagan statue
16. Large jug
17. Lay off (staff)
20. Circumstances
23. Sharp (pain)
24. Dependable
25. Makes beer

DOWN
1. Followed orders
2. Affirm
3. Possess
4. French pancake
5. As stated by, ... to
6. Beneficial
9. Endures
11. Customers
13. Maiden name indicator
15. Sports stadium
16. Guarantee
18. Refuges
19. Air traffic monitor
21. Maladies
22. Wound blemish

Crossword 135

ACROSS
1. Transported
5. Repel, ... off
7. Doe's mate
8. Conceited
9. Sorrowful poem
12. Diminishes
15. Strangely
19. Beeped (horn)
21. Moved ahead
22. Genuine
23. Shrill barks
24. Sprayed

DOWN
1. Royal home
2. Indistinct
3. Leavening agent
4. Ridicule
5. Bets
6. Obligations
10. Method
11. In the area of
12. Produce (egg)
13. Japanese-style wrestling
14. Radiate
15. Squeamish
16. Evenly matches
17. Cavalry spears
18. Befuddled
19. Of sea phases
20. Storybook monsters

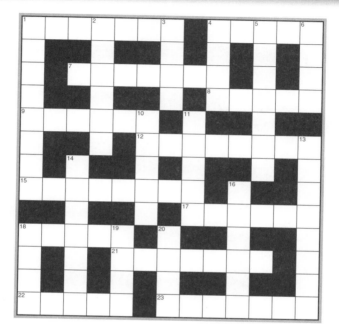

ACROSS

1. Clap
4. Slow-moving mammal
7. Able to be read
8. Get to feet
9. Sewing cotton
12. Studied closely
15. Leave place of danger
17. Harvester
18. Taunt
21. Quantities
22. Splashes (through)
23. Yapping in pain

DOWN

1. Aircraft height
2. Looked sneeringly
3. Sponges lightly
4. Witnesses
5. Gains possession of
6. Head covering
10. Time lag
11. More secure
13. Towering over
14. Marched in procession
16. Portable computer
18. Defrost
19. Grain tips
20. Small bunch of flowers

Crossword 137

ACROSS
1. Disconcert
4. Was able to
7. Swindle
8. Fill with joy
9. Soothed
12. Undo (belt)
15. Lack of hearing
17. Discreet suggestion, ... hint
18. Small but significant role
21. Technical drawing
22. Smoke tendrils
23. Shut & opened eyes

DOWN
1. Vacant
2. Smoothly
3. Historical ages
4. Relinquish (land)
5. Unloads (suitcase)
6. ... & duchess
10. Deceives
11. Chasm
13. Surpassed
14. Mallets
16. Derive
18. Masticate
19. Gambling chances
20. Part of arrow

ACROSS

1. Floating free
5. States further
7. Tiny particles
8. Ready to harvest
9. Utters
10. Buddhist fate
11. Sloping channels
13. Curved-bill wading bird
14. Clothes maker
18. Hurry
21. Beach surface
22. Of the supernatural
24. Put off
25. Heredity unit
26. Long (for)
27. Chosen direction
28. Unprocessed minerals
29. Horse-bucking shows

DOWN

1. Peach-like fruit
2. Incompetent
3. Army vehicles
4. Give sustenance to
5. Accosts
6. Dawn to dusk
12. Self-pride
15. Unpaid sportsman
16. Portable steps
17. Serene
19. Crescent
20. Chatters idly
22. Requisition
23. Managed

Crossword **139**

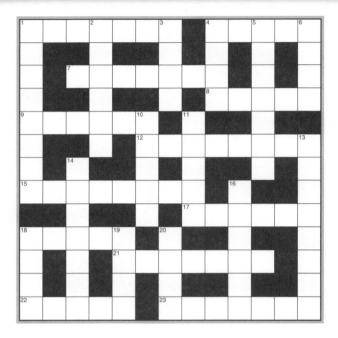

ACROSS
1. Made minor adjustments to
4. Small trumpet
7. Of the stars
8. Immerses
9. Ring of flowers
12. Letter jumbles
15. Magnificence
17. Remained
18. Parish minister
21. Weaponless
22. Unadventurous
23. Swept

DOWN
1. Tossing
2. Celestial
3. Type of herb
4. Forbids entry
5. Escape vehicle, ... car
6. Female sheep
10. Dislikes
11. Twos
13. Made unhappy
14. Eye cosmetic
16. Stroke fondly
18. Contests, ... with
19. Regretted
20. Curved hook

ACROSS
1. As it sounds
5. Small pool
7. Sharp twinge
8. Denied ownership of
9. Raises spirits of
12. Shade of red
15. Upper limit
19. Contemptuous looks
21. Computer-based catalogue

22. Cylinder
23. Unclothed
24. Exhibits

DOWN
1. Burst
2. Opposite of day
3. Ocean phases
4. Of the universe
5. Fine particles
6. Subtract
10. Tip of triangle

11. Dutch cheese
12. Amount
13. Yemen port
14. Ancient harp
15. Provoke to anger
16. Inherited
17. Voluntary (work)
18. Evaluate
19. Simmers
20. Throw out

Crossword **141**

ACROSS
1. Sleepily
5. Incapacitate
7. Vocal solo
8. Moved restlessly
9. Puzzling question
12. Headache remedy
15. Conflicted (with)
19. Legendary
21. Progressed
22. Male monarch
23. Parched
24. Scientific ideas

DOWN
1. Outlines
2. Introduces to solid food
3. Deduce
4. Sings alpine-style
5. Swiss cereal
6. Up-to-date
10. Greenish blue
11. Engrave
12. In addition
13. Cougar
14. Spool
15. Droning insect
16. Thread
17. Draw out
18. Maxims
19. Soft toffee
20. Bread maker

Crossword 142

ACROSS
1. Absconders
5. Always
7. Tiny branch
8. Not scared
9. Dehydration symptom
12. Plods
15. Vulgar
19. More orderly
21. Very distressing
22. Loan
23. Light sleeps
24. Laterally

DOWN
1. Gyrate
2. Hostility
3. Mature
4. Beard trimmer
5. Fetching task
6. FM receivers
10. Woes
11. Confident
12. Musical, ... Wizard Of Oz
13. Encourage
14. Squall
15. Life gas
16. Desert animals
17. Sheer hosiery
18. Wears away
19. Nuzzled
20. Let

Crossword **143**

ACROSS
1. Extra
4. Avarice
7. Helsinki is there
8. Burn with steam
9. Gradually develop
12. Small settlements
15. Role models
17. Australian marsupials
18. Damages
21. Citrus fruits
22. Precise
23. Well-educated

DOWN
1. Prison term
2. Prudishly
3. Exchange
4. Deities
5. Suspension of commerce
6. Title document
10. Wicked wrongs
11. Drink container
13. Abated
14. Hot spice
16. Vocation
18. Cross-country walk
19. Chimney dirt
20. Sphere

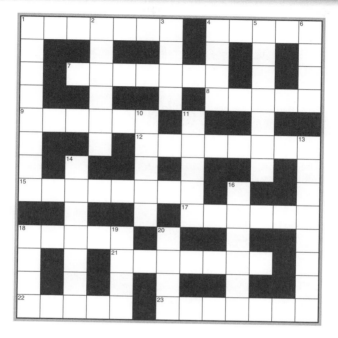

ACROSS

1. Leftover piece
4. Sentry
7. Steering mechanism
8. Dining bench
9. Mourn
12. Evilly
15. Boiled gently
17. Equine complex
18. Wine fruit
21. Muslim veil
22. Fills with air, ... up
23. Mislead

DOWN

1. Asylum seekers
2. Lasso loops
3. Make weary
4. Gold leaf
5. Anyone
6. Rounded roof
10. Large jugs
11. Corrosive substances
13. Christmas season
14. Official trade ban
16. Enchantress, femme ...
18. Insincere (of speech)
19. Detectives, private ...
20. Availed oneself of

Crossword 145

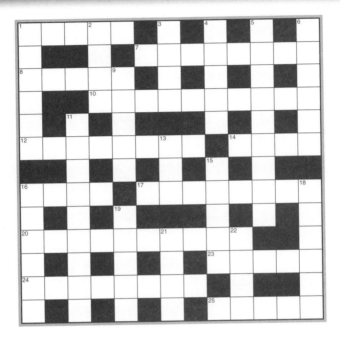

ACROSS
1. Large jet plane
7. Kingdom
8. Light purple
10. Worst behaved
12. Twice radius
14. Contented cat's sound
16. Writes, ... down
17. Fuse switches, circuit ...
20. Rebuking
23. Small meal
24. Makes more exciting
25. Pale with shock

DOWN
1. Forsaken at altar
2. Grain husks
3. Lengthy
4. Delicious
5. Itineraries
6. Pearl-bearer
9. Soap bars
11. Not wholly
13. Go astray
15. Showers heavily
16. Book cover
18. Take ill
19. Cooking range
21. Mail (off)
22. Wildebeests

ACROSS
1. Without sound
5. Anchor (boat)
7. Grand-scale
8. Fell to pieces
9. Biblical prayers
12. Rises
15. Looser
19. Halts
21. Luxuriously self-indulgent
22. Gambling cubes
23. Symbol of peace
24. Snakes

DOWN
1. Hibernates
2. Do well (at)
3. Sewn folds
4. Teenagers
5. Movable
6. Half-diameter
10. Greenish-blue
11. Perfume ingredient
12. House cooler, ... conditioner
13. Manage
14. Pen tips
15. Screened from sun
16. Bring into existence
17. Forces out
18. Resources
19. Supply food
20. Confuse

Crossword **147**

ACROSS
1. Most extended
4. Speak publicly
7. Armed conflict
8. Oxen harnesses
9. Parried, ... off
12. Dreams up
15. Makes happier
17. Mentally demanding
18. Yellow gemstone
21. Gave too much food to
22. Forewarnings
23. Sold on street

DOWN
1. Vaulting game
2. Protects
3. Warty amphibian
4. Follow orders
5. Stimulates
6. Historical ages
10. Cut into cubes
11. Ribs to hips region
13. Snubbed
14. Frog stage
16. Surpass
18. Mexican snack
19. Wildlife enclosures
20. Assistance

ACROSS
1. Inundates
5. Icy rain
7. Buddhist fate
8. Midday
9. Donation
10. Inanimate object
11. Becomes informed
13. Scantiness
14. Painted roughly
18. Neglect
21. Wheel spindle
22. Scratched
24. Of sound
25. Angler's barb
26. Swerve
27. Select by voting
28. Soviet states (1,1,1,1)
29. Exclusively

DOWN
1. Touched affectionately
2. Possessor
3. Satirical sketches
4. Drew off water from
5. Argues over price
6. Affects with disease
12. Formerly known as
15. Nervously tense
16. More dismal
17. River Jordan lake (4,3)
19. Sick
20. Mature in years
22. Young male horses
23. Metal-working block

Crossword **149**

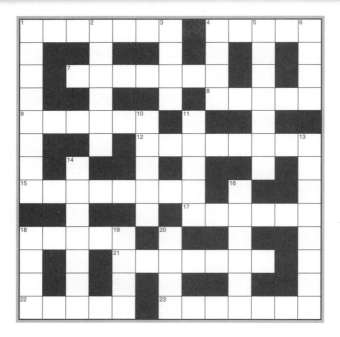

ACROSS
1. Of plants
4. Polluted
7. Strain
8. Talent
9. Widen (pupils)
12. Local languages
15. Proceeds (from)
17. Shouted
18. Connected to current
21. Reactor fuel
22. Dizzy
23. Thoroughly informed

DOWN
1. Apply retrospectively
2. Stadiums
3. Voucher
4. Damp & cold
5. Return bout
6. Nucleus of egg
10. Prepares (newspaper)
11. Viola flower
13. Followed closely
14. Wed
16. Shirt
18. Flight limb
19. Properly
20. Paint roughly

ACROSS

1. Go sour (of milk)
5. Focal points
7. Aristocratic
8. Brink
9. Extended family
10. Middle
11. Immensely
13. Monkey relatives
14. Synagogue ministers
18. Lubrication
21. Operator
22. Snow shelters
24. Tolerate
25. Dole (out)
26. Grape drink
27. Of the kidneys
28. Smell strongly
29. Wiliest

DOWN

1. Butcher's knife
2. Resided
3. Hostile opponent
4. Complying with, ... by
5. Unit of land
6. Dam-building creatures
12. Hawaiian garland
15. Severely simple
16. Run amok, go ...
17. Joint injuries
19. Material scrap
20. Most effortless
22. Pop stars
23. Meek

Crossword 151

ACROSS

1. More dependable
5. Cleaning agent, caustic ...
7. Advance
8. Fruit groves
9. Pleasantly
12. Retailers
15. Most virtuous
19. Spiritualist's meeting
21. Study of religion
22. Long story
23. Wet weather
24. Spookiness

DOWN

1. Skill
2. Because
3. Tusk material
4. Say from memory
5. Humiliated
6. Resources
10. Barber's tool
11. Sit idly
12. Winery fermentation tank
13. Roman IX
14. Bullocks
15. Flower syrup
16. Coral island lake
17. Walked
18. Sums up
19. Sneakier
20. Malicious fire-setting

ACROSS
1. Metal container
5. Produced (egg)
7. Minuscule amount
8. Octopus arm
9. Construes
12. Rupturing (muscle)
15. Fragility
19. Drying cloths
21. Numbers
22. Door handle
23. Unchanged, the ...
24. Supervisor

DOWN
1. Film reviewer
2. Cross
3. Ballet dresses
4. Go back on deal
5. Ruler
6. Tinting
10. Hopping parasite
11. Train track
12. Attempt
13. As well
14. Tiny landmass
15. Sides
16. Obstruct
17. Ketchup, ... sauce
18. Weather map line
19. Oral sense
20. Rouses

Crossword **153**

ACROSS
1. Member of coven
7. Denied
8. Brindled cat
10. Specially tagging
12. Spanking
14. Beats tennis opponent with serve
16. Prepare food
17. Purified
20. Significant
23. Golfer's two under par
24. Ascending
25. Rock shelf

DOWN
1. Irrigates
2. Six-sided figure
3. Translucent covering
4. Fungus seed
5. Flight of steps
6. Proverbs
9. Pulls with a jerk
11. Uninterrupted (vista)
13. No score
15. Worth
16. Joke-tellers
18. Remove (from text)
19. State of suspension
21. Percussion instrument
22. Utah's Salt ... City

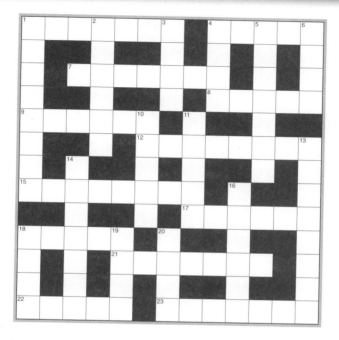

ACROSS
1. Marred
4. Military store
7. Flight staff
8. Illustrious
9. Joined forces, ... up
12. Re-evaluate
15. Newspaper caption
17. Detest
18. Succumb
21. Praised highly
22. Oppressed
23. Sighing sleepily

DOWN
1. Nervous
2. Colloquialisms
3. Be brave enough
4. Not up
5. Complication
6. Confiscate
10. Storm water pipe
11. Judge's hammer
13. Saying "a-tishoo"
14. Hesitated
16. Inn
18. Shout
19. Cult actor, James ...
20. Simple

Crossword **155**

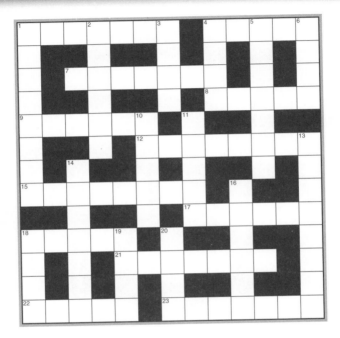

ACROSS
1. Sighing sleepily
4. Acted wordlessly
7. Plush
8. Artist's stand
9. Me
12. Brave
15. Rush headlong (of herd)
17. Thundered
18. Skin-diving gear
21. Infectious viral disease
22. Water lily
23. Northern sea fish

DOWN
1. Face veils
2. Niece & ...
3. Clarified butter
4. Breed (with)
5. Car race official
6. Dress-up toy
10. Blends by melting
11. Bread maker
13. Loitering
14. Most indistinct
16. Profession
18. Dirt
19. Sound boosters
20. Whip stroke

ACROSS
1. Thin dagger
5. Not this, but ...
7. Opera solo
8. Conceited
9. Muscle contractions
12. Japanese hostesses
15. Stiff felt hats
19. Tags
21. Towards the back
22. Alleged spy, ... Hari
23. Require
24. Enjoyment

DOWN
1. Scant
2. Burdens
3. Cylinders
4. Citrus fruit
5. Book names
6. Claws
10. Once again
11. Donkey/horse cross
12. Poison with fumes
13. Minuscule amount
14. Charter
15. Devoid of vegetation
16. Stared
17. Refurbish
18. Large property
19. Narrow shelf
20. Explosive weapons

Crossword **157**

ACROSS
1. Energetic
4. Level with another surface
7. Stir up
8. Exhibited
9. Cried in pain
12. Planned
15. Issued (from)
17. Sailing boats
18. Tropical fruit
21. Careful examination
22. Peeled
23. Warrant

DOWN
1. Destroy large portion of (group)
2. Heart disease symptom
3. Clothed
4. Tuition costs
5. Removes (bullets from gun)
6. Rhinoceros spike
10. Weight-loss regimes
11. Look at closely
13. Deter
14. Administrator
16. Rasp
18. Fight for air
19. Copied
20. Parched

ACROSS
1. Fronting
5. Snare
7. Senseless (comment)
8. Long and limp (hair)
9. Sport squad
10. Feel with fingers
11. Positive electrodes
13. Saga
14. Barked
18. Plan
21. Word indicating action
22. Meet the cost of
24. Mild-tasting
25. Room divider
26. Cessation
27. Put in (data)
28. Table parts
29. Older people

DOWN
1. Mistaken belief
2. Irritated
3. Presents
4. Gave military greeting
5. Ties up
6. Astonishing
12. Night before
15. Par
16. Small round stones
17. Leaves
19. Folklore creature
20. Nodes
22. Worship
23. Manicured (nails)

Crossword **159**

ACROSS
1. Orders
5. Green gemstone
7. Reservoir
8. Insulin-deficient person
9. Alternate ones
12. Spanned
15. Char
19. Get free
21. Hollow out
22. Wild cat
23. Compass point
24. Abandoned

DOWN
1. Universe
2. Canadian leaf symbol
3. Artist's naked models
4. Ice performer
5. Mocked
6. Go too far
10. Hawaiian dance
11. Peril
12. Receptacle
13. Charged particles
14. Carnival
15. Gentle wind
16. Deep blue pigment
17. Enlarge
18. Held for trial, on ...
19. Pitchers
20. Playful skip

Crossword **160**

ACROSS
1. Muslim veil
4. Subdue (riot)
7. College certificate
8. Crave, ... for
9. Led
12. No longer in style
15. Slenderness
17. Funeral vehicle
18. Shopping mall
21. Notorious affair
22. Nips with beak
23. Machine-driven

DOWN
1. Young in appearance
2. Coiffure
3. Understand
4. Dock
5. Messages to run
6. Pork cut
10. Lavished affection (on)
11. Hidden supply
13. Deranged
14. Demonic
16. Cope
18. Stage-play item
19. Inquires
20. Sleep in tent

Crossword **161**

ACROSS

1. Men's hairdresser
5. Applies with pats
7. Avoid (capture)
8. Statistics
9. Taverns
10. Piece of glowing coal
11. Mosquito or bee
13. Part of eye
14. Caper
18. Fume angrily
21. Lend
22. Male's partner
24. Bird of prey
25. Restaurant cook
26. Unconscious state
27. Freezing over
28. Horse's gait
29. Most recent

DOWN

1. Making offer
2. Knife's cutting edge
3. Adjust (watch)
4. Wagers
5. Take away from, ... of
6. Infantile
12. Dove call
15. One more
16. Advantage
17. Lethargic
19. Mother sheep
20. Gracefully stylish
22. Pretend
23. South American parrot

ACROSS
1. Detect
5. Prods sharply
7. Exaggeratedly masculine
8. Defined region
9. Seepage
10. Shine
11. Bee's liquid harvest
13. Single object
14. Carnivores, meat ...
18. Most painful
21. Cougar
22. Stood on hind legs
24. Terminate
25. Days of yore, the ...
26. Graceful bird
27. Clear
28. Refuse to admit
29. Wool clippers

DOWN
1. Throat capsule
2. Adroit
3. Piece of glowing coal
4. Frozen water spikes
5. Merrier
6. Sportsmen's jackets
12. Ventilate
15. Flatter to excess
16. Precisely
17. Graze
19. Primary number
20. News
22. Splits apart
23. Supermarket lane

Crossword **163**

ACROSS
1. Integral
7. Unstable
8. Shrewd
10. Jingling percussion instrument
12. Meat-soaking mixture
14. Coral shipping hazard
16. Metropolis
17. Spellbinding
20. Sailor's skill
23. Lolled
24. Perceiving
25. Variety of animal

DOWN
1. Airless space
2. Parent's sister
3. Deliberately ignore
4. Black ale
5. Policy statement
6. Me
9. Spun threads
11. Prolongs
13. Arid
15. Escargot
16. Las Vegas establishment
18. Scolded
19. Knight's spear
21. Transmitted
22. Set of two

Crossword **164**

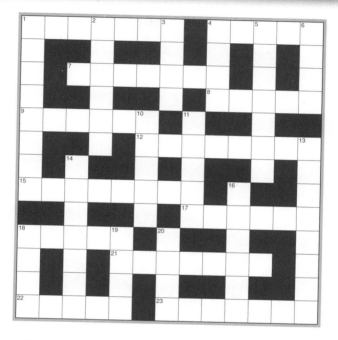

ACROSS

1. Turned outwards
4. Carpentry clamps
7. Amount of film
8. Ire
9. Rotate
12. State of perplexity
15. Preparing
17. Led Zeppelin classic, Stairway To ...
18. Tobacco item
21. External
22. Rectify
23. End result

DOWN

1. Illegal importer
2. Lacking ethics
3. College head
4. Opinion
5. Drumming insects
6. Weary moan
10. Furnish with supplies
11. Giggle
13. Most junior
14. Luggage
16. Passed (over)
18. Havana is there
19. Highway
20. Upon

Crossword **165**

ACROSS
1. Cutting utensil
7. Most rigid
8. Postage sticker
10. Making longer
12. Furthest back
14. Tiny insects
16. Metric weight unit
17. Incapacitated
20. Unnecessarily
23. Adolescent
24. Prominence
25. Earlier

DOWN
1. Jewish food custom
2. Celebrity status
3. Stupefy
4. Edible innards
5. Boldly
6. Periods of growth
9. Stone fruits
11. Medical support worker
13. Slide on snow
15. Unhappily
16. Armed gangsters
18. Act indecisively
19. Narrow lane
21. Nauseous
22. Belonging to you

ACROSS
1. Droning insect
5. Contented
7. Taunt
8. Fluent & insincere
9. Rip
10. Unsuitable
11. Sensual
13. Tropical wading bird
14. Bicycle for two
18. Hire (employee)
21. Canned fish
22. Short-sighted
24. Hang
25. Green gemstone
26. Dull thump
27. Nook
28. Domestic fowls
29. Moved back and forth

DOWN
1. Most guarded
2. Monastery head
3. Room beneath a roof
4. Due (of money)
5. Procuring
6. Lessening
12. Fury
15. Flatter to excess
16. Numbs
17. Sovereign ruler
19. "No" vote
20. Encrypted
22. Gauge
23. Of the eyes

Crossword 167

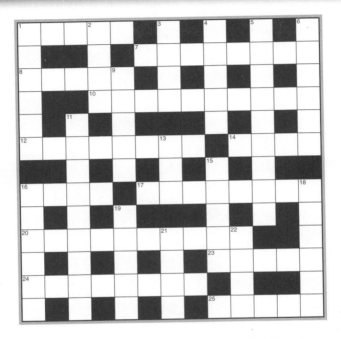

ACROSS
1. Heats up
7. Marooned
8. Step (on)
10. Alcohol abstinence
12. Rekindle
14. Arm or leg
16. Wharf
17. Hatchet
20. Meteorologist
23. Determined age of (fossil)
24. Facts as proof
25. Transparent

DOWN
1. Shrivel
2. Castle ditch
3. Come to a halt
4. Couples
5. The very same
6. Verb modifier
9. Dental caries, tooth ...
11. Artificial sweetener
13. Sense of self
15. Cold side dish
16. Broke (of day)
18. More generous
19. Potter's turning device
21. Display shelf
22. Carpentry spike

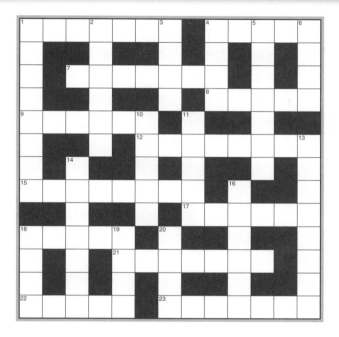

ACROSS

1. Left unoccupied
4. Metropolitan
7. Looked briefly
8. Unconcealed
9. Alpine melodies
12. Giving therapy to
15. Technical drawings
17. Howled shrilly
18. Singer, ... Sinatra
21. Slipped by
22. Estimate
23. Throat capsule

DOWN

1. Grape-growing property
2. Wartime friends
3. Ship's floor
4. Unbutton
5. Gain
6. Afterwards
10. Weasel-like creature
11. Untidy
13. Obtain degree
14. Flair
16. Claim
18. Adult tadpole
19. Lock openers
20. Lamenting cry

Crossword **169**

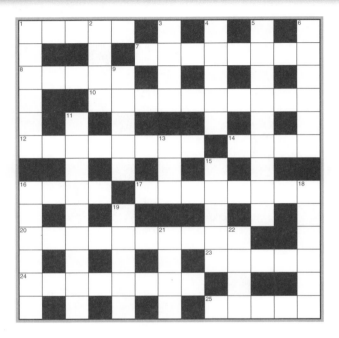

ACROSS
1. Take oath
7. Plane-jump sportsman
8. Phrase
10. Impartiality
12. Gaining knowledge
14. Recited
16. Niggles
17. Of metal
20. Countryside paintings
23. Foolishly idealistic
24. Puffed up
25. Genre

DOWN
1. Swirl
2. Unknown writer
3. Satirical sketch
4. Notions
5. Escapable
6. Tattered
9. Intends
11. Type of dive
13. Named before marriage
15. Shelter
16. Set in (design)
18. Cheddar or Edam
19. Hollywood award statuette
21. Gorillas or chimpanzees
22. Common seasoning

ACROSS

1. Blossom part
7. Illicit
8. Sixteenth of pound
10. Fast food snacks
12. Slimness
14. Tie with rope
16. Annoys constantly
17. Without deviation
20. Bring into accord
23. Frosting
24. Quick drawings
25. Noxious

DOWN

1. Launch forward
2. Curved span
3. Rebuff
4. Egypt's capital
5. Religious gifts
6. Shut
9. Receives as salary
11. Tidal zone trees
13. Movie filming area
15. Prickly desert plants
16. Kindest
18. Disastrous
19. Official decree
21. Necessity
22. Reflected sound

Crossword 171

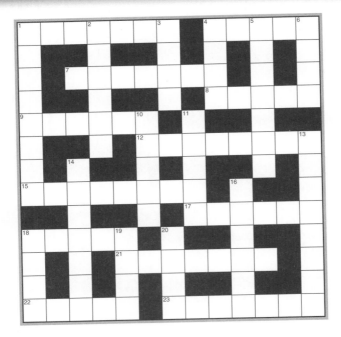

ACROSS
1. Commonplace
4. Regal
7. Watched over
8. Fantastic
9. Shadows (prey)
12. Celibate (relationship)
15. Re-emerge
17. Gazed fixedly
18. Thoroughfares
21. Animal hide material
22. South American parrot
23. Insect, ... mantis

DOWN
1. Major celebrity
2. Tennis score, ... fault
3. Small whirlpool
4. Birch canes
5. Barking shrilly
6. Suggestive grin
10. Espionage agents
11. Twos
13. Going sour (of milk)
14. Demonic
16. Security
18. Wander
19. Not fast
20. Elevated walkway

ACROSS
1. Most useful
5. Parsley or sage
7. Wildebeests
8. Tolerable
9. Laden
12. Happened (upon)
15. Suffocated in water
19. Aimless stroll
21. Courted
22. Fairy's rod
23. Wearing footwear
24. Defrauded

DOWN
1. Greatly
2. Gave medicine to
3. Lodge firmly
4. Roofing grass
5. Utter bliss
6. Concocted
10. In addition
11. All square
12. Oily fish
13. Greenish blue
14. Rein in
15. Wreckage
16. Harry Potter is one
17. Ejects
18. Married
19. Diameter halves
20. Cut (lawn)

Crossword 173

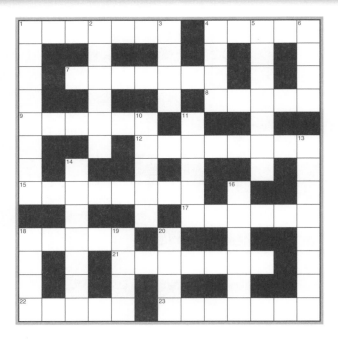

ACROSS

1. Pouring out
4. Listened to
7. Wound wrapping
8. Sketches
9. Property wrecker
12. Expecting
15. Greatness
17. Tooth covering
18. Hefty
21. Rescued disaster victim
22. Of the sun
23. Sighing sleepily

DOWN

1. Lamenting
2. Amasses stock
3. Mountain animal
4. Take note of
5. Water-related
6. Weirs
10. Rubber
11. Chaplain
13. Interrogating
14. Sunshade
16. Inn
18. Beer ingredient
19. 12-month period
20. Fluctuate

Crossword 174

ACROSS
1. More nauseous
5. Not stiff
7. Wicked
8. Walked unsteadily
9. Wrestle
12. Searched (body)
15. Doubt innocence of
19. Rode bicycle
21. Redraw
22. Fish breathing organ
23. (To) which person?
24. Small birds

DOWN
1. Expeditions
2. Collection of charts
3. Matter
4. Book user
5. Defames
6. Cushioned
10. Scatters (seeds)
11. Early guitar
12. Be the right size for
13. Very black
14. Execute
15. Misery
16. Cough mucus
17. Assertions
18. Grown-ups
19. Latin American hand drum
20. Tobacco product

Crossword **175**

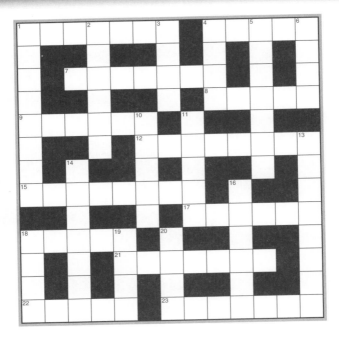

ACROSS
1. Genetically altered
4. Rubbed lightly
7. Protest banner
8. Pass (legislation)
9. Heathens
12. Pants
15. Fishing vessels
17. Deeply desires
18. Ear test, ... examination
21. Citrus fruits
22. Strange
23. Enormous

DOWN
1. Squandered
2. Not sinking
3. Haul
4. Broad
5. Royal homes
6. Song for two
10. Hard iron alloy
11. Loud
13. Bright weather
14. Bearer (of disease)
16. Thin biscuits
18. Wheel shaft
19. Taste defeat
20. Coconut tree

ACROSS
1. Unspoken
5. Taunt
7. Surpass
8. Fictional spy, James ...
9. Fills with reverence
10. Clergyman
11. Despise
13. Scamps
14. Game park tour
18. Cloyingly sweet
21. Pet's parasite
22. Straighten out
24. Fewest
25. Serving platter
26. Reverse the effects of
27. Part of play
28. Body fluid lump
29. Red gems

DOWN
1. Unfastens (door)
2. Accounts check
3. Probe
4. Frozen drips
5. Scowling
6. Paging device
12. That lady
15. Unusual sensitivity
16. Market researcher
17. Transfixes
19. Decorative garden pot
20. Golden hues
22. Absolute
23. Morsel

Crossword 177

ACROSS
1. Wily
5. Pen tips
7. Lead-in
8. Brave man
9. On an occasion
10. Lazed
11. Have effect (on)
13. Scalp parasites
14. Oversee
18. Dress ribbons
21. Tropical tree
22. More profound
24. Irritating to the skin
25. Terrace level
26. Cattle prod
27. Run off to marry
28. Old
29. Becomes faster, ... up

DOWN
1. Religious non-belief
2. Local vegetation
3. Extent
4. Sloping typeface
5. Asian food items
6. Tour de France vehicle
12. Wheel tooth
15. Astounding
16. Respected
17. Pilot safety aid, ... seat
19. Beer
20. Long steps
22. Dutch sea walls
23. Golfer's two under par

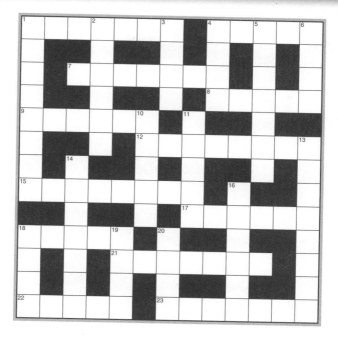

ACROSS
1. Visual trick,
   ... illusion
4. Conscious
7. Shortfall
8. Different
9. Lubricant
12. Small-style
    newspapers
15. Tip
17. Wriggle
18. Urge to action
21. Not balanced
22. Resided
23. Showed (to seat)

DOWN
1. Eager to please
2. Frozen polar cover
3. Good fortune
4. Singing voice
5. Antiquated
6. Pitcher
10. Moral principle
11. Follows directives
13. Boiled gently
14. Dracula is one
16. Undergo genetic
    change
18. Chilled
19. Strong desire
20. Restaurant list

Crossword 179

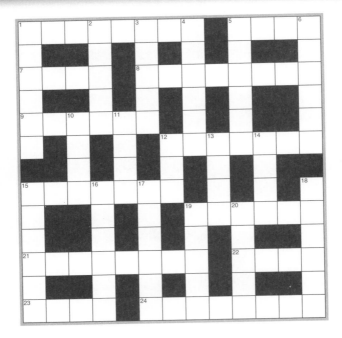

ACROSS

1. Endures longer than
5. Inactive
7. Hawaiian dance
8. Massaging
9. Wandered
12. Relate (story)
15. Cooked in juices
19. Bellowed
21. Squid
22. Chinese design system, feng ...
23. Sand hill
24. Eagerness

DOWN

1. Alternatives
2. Cloud of insects
3. Requested, ... for
4. Spanish rest period
5. Undercover (venue)
6. Involve (in)
10. Zone
11. Supplements, ... out
12. Assent with head
13. Complete again
14. At a distance
15. Reinforced
16. Prison occupant
17. Venture forth
18. Lets in
19. Elevate
20. Fire crime

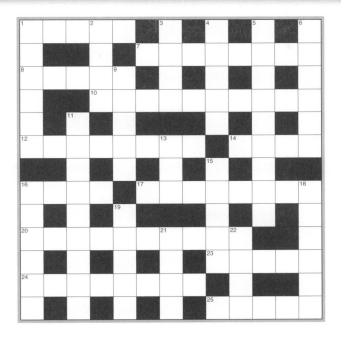

ACROSS
1. Fertile desert spot
7. Private
8. Enticed
10. Senior churchman
12. Restate
14. Egyptian snakes
16. Let fall
17. Gained
20. Without commander
23. Felt pain
24. Clutching
25. Entertain

DOWN
1. More greasy
2. Notion
3. Netting fabric
4. On the move
5. Expressing keenness (over)
6. Flees to wed
9. Flow with tide
11. Wide views
13. Large rodent
15. Light timber
16. Flood
18. Absent-minded scribble
19. Parsley & mint
21. Surgical dressing
22. Floating filth

Crossword **181**

ACROSS
1. Orchestral composition
5. Animal foot
7. Small drop
8. Vacations
9. Expedition head
12. Stuck (to)
15. Angered
19. Made airtight
21. Deviated
22. Dinner chime
23. Retailed
24. Frees from blame

DOWN
1. Jockey's seat
2. Pumped through tube
3. Alternate
4. Shouted
5. Crowd together
6. Abstained from food
10. Actor, ... Alda
11. Effortless
12. Also
13. Possess
14. Fishing spool
15. Incidental comments
16. Insult
17. Puzzle
18. Proverbs
19. Sports teams
20. Protector, guardian ...

ACROSS
1. Pakistan's ... Pass
5. Bird's bill
7. Senior
8. Fencing sword
9. Upper limbs
10. Long claw
11. Secretes
13. Be brave enough
14. Leafy side dishes
18. Comforting squeeze
21. Parsley or mint
22. Innate
24. Riled
25. Chesspiece
26. Wild pig
27. Surpass
28. Hawaiian garlands
29. Threw

DOWN
1. Zoo custodians
2. Mix
3. Hires out
4. Perfect
5. Marked (cattle)
6. Navy chief
12. Finish
15. Normal
16. Pure white animals
17. Eyeball hollows
19. Large vase
20. Survived
22. Simpleton
23. Infants

Crossword 183

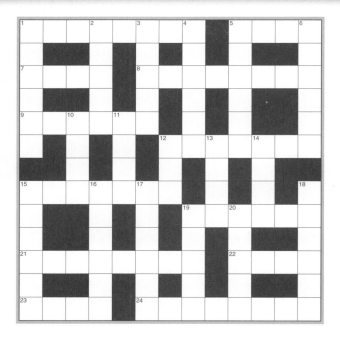

ACROSS
1. Intermixing
5. Word indicating action
7. Climbing plant
8. Mentally pictured
9. Tidily
12. Take dimensions of
15. Ballroom dance
19. To wit
21. Progresses
22. Blood vessel
23. Deciduous trees
24. Has misgivings about

DOWN
1. Budging
2. The ... Wall of China
3. Coldly
4. Type of beard
5. Vocal sounds
6. Dress top
10. Tip of triangle
11. Animal den
12. Small floor covering
13. Greenish-blue
14. Strong desire
15. Rummage
16. Sums
17. Liquid units, fluid ...
18. African scavengers
19. Baby bird shelters
20. Hollywood production

ACROSS
1. Watch out!
5. Deck mop
7. Nocturnal hours
8. Wren or jay
9. Imperial unit
10. Precipice
11. Bring from overseas
13. Jar tops
14. Doled (out)
18. Abandonment
21. Hint
22. Slid on ice
24. Coronet
25. Ancestry, family ...
26. Grizzly animal
27. Riding & roping show
28. Tints
29. Deadened

DOWN
1. Infantile
2. Of sound
3. Put into effect
4. Set fire to
5. Represses
6. Shopping walkways
12. Caviar
15. Sensitivity to substance
16. Weight watchers
17. Insists on
19. Annoy
20. Suffered
22. Beauty establishment
23. Stamp book

Crossword **185**

ACROSS
1. Intricately decorated
5. Castle water barrier
7. Astonish
8. Famous Italian tower city
9. Melt
10. Depart
11. Positive electrodes
13. Elliptic
14. Went by yacht
18. Readjusts (clock)
21. Expel (lava)
22. Underground stems
24. Break into pieces
25. Honolulu's island
26. Prod
27. Bury
28. Chair
29. Eludes

DOWN
1. Deprives of parents
2. Trophy
3. Noblemen
4. Spanish bullfighter
5. Small celestial bodies
6. Emphatic
12. Sight organ
15. Pacify
16. Legal action
17. Ruling family
19. Australian bird
20. Siblings
22. Bronze medal position
23. Two-footed creature

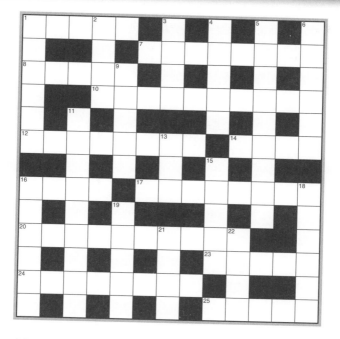

ACROSS
1. Jury
7. Dampness of air
8. Ballet skirts
10. Portable stairs
12. Roofs with straw
14. Expired
16. Submerged
17. Evangelist
20. Logos
23. Dog's cries
24. Regretfully
25. Performed slalom

DOWN
1. Powerful
2. Australian birds
3. Hindquarters
4. Travel permits
5. Retrospective wisdom
6. Crossbreed
9. Shop supplies
11. Cloud moisture
13. Wheat spike
15. Tall & skinny
16. Parody
18. Elevated
19. Lists of meals
21. Competently
22. Search for

Crossword 187

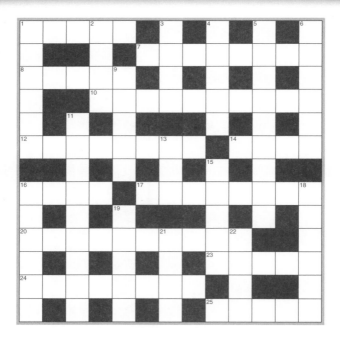

ACROSS
1. Fruit liquid
7. Openly
8. Drains (udder)
10. Settlement overseas
12. Permitting
14. Touch at one end
16. As well
17. Exerted
20. Range of known words

23. Spun threads
24. Outrageous incidents
25. Ran in neutral

DOWN
1. Mixture
2. Coal by-product
3. Sharp taste
4. Standard of perfection
5. Improvising (2-7)

6. Swan chick
9. Diminutive
11. Sleeveless garment
13. Few, ... many
15. Furry
16. Give counsel to
18. Extinguished
19. Living quarters
21. Sit in relaxed way
22. Three feet

ACROSS

1. Ignite
5. Martial art
7. Formerly
8. Railway bridges
9. Conquering hero
12. Exerted force
15. Tom Cruise film, ... *Sky*
19. Classified
21. Explosive in nature
22. Tooth pain
23. Frog relative
24. Precious rock

DOWN

1. Gradually develop
2. Clumsy
3. Springboard athlete
4. Pencil-mark remover
5. Short excursions
6. Unseated
10. Maize
11. Ellipse
12. Pod vegetable
13. Always
14. Wearing shoes
15. Soft napped fabric
16. Set into surface
17. Existing
18. Cling (to)
19. Glow
20. Separately

Crossword **189**

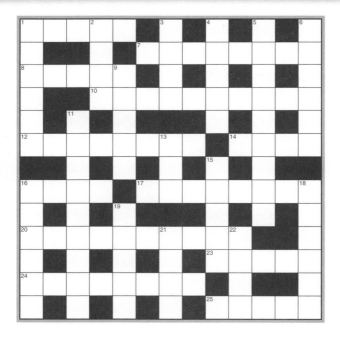

ACROSS
1. Opposite of rural
7. Daughter's child
8. Common
10. Juveniles
12. Complete disorder
14. Rushed
16. Glass pots
17. Looking very undernourished
20. Significant
23. Brought under control
24. Most fortunate
25. Sense of the absurd

DOWN
1. Dethrones
2. Not here
3. Wide smile
4. Grind (teeth) together
5. Bone specialist
6. Unexpended
9. Hotel foyer
11. Male family head
13. Large deer
15. Disobey (rules)
16. Mixture
18. Indecently
19. Inflexible
21. Deep wound
22. Den

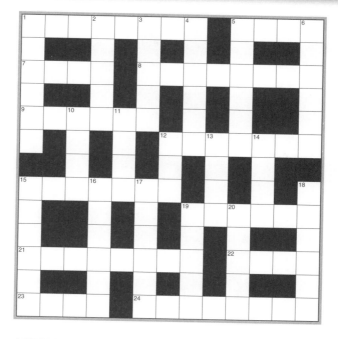

ACROSS
1. Progressed
5. Give up
7. Incursion
8. Insulin-deficient person
9. Come to notice
12. Held tightly
15. Utterly
19. Lewd man
21. Bordering on, ... to
22. Orange-peel lining
23. Canned fish
24. AWOL soldier

DOWN
1. Pilots
2. Viper
3. Obtain by begging
4. Sliding shelf
5. Kings' wives
6. Marked as correct
10. Radiate
11. Young woman
12. Anchoring rope
13. Pimple rash
14. Nudge
15. Cruel ruler
16. Spanish fleet
17. Folk hero
18. Arrow marksman
19. Type of lily
20. Frolic

Crossword **191**

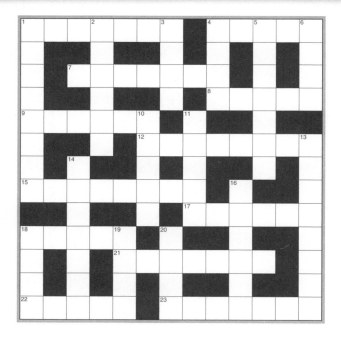

ACROSS
1. Asked
4. Rouse
7. Sneered
8. Moves to & fro
9. Deeply desires
12. Clothing made of wool
15. Rivers of ice
17. Eluded (capture)
18. Flooded (of decks)
21. Citrus fruits
22. Playing-card Jack
23. Relaxation time

DOWN
1. Suggesting
2. Becomes liable for
3. Dexterous
4. Tallies
5. Soothed
6. Australian birds
10. Snow sportsperson
11. Remove soap from
13. Edge of highway
14. Indonesian capital
16. Falters
18. Go wild, run ...
19. Tubing
20. Bouncing toy

ACROSS

1. To the point
5. Expired
7. Large tooth
8. Questioner
9. Ogled, ... at
12. Referee's device
15. Line of hereditary rulers
19. Burglaries
21. Financial
22. Stupor
23. Decoy
24. Makes stable

DOWN

1. Sweepstake
2. Enthusiastic
3. In front
4. Roofing grass
5. Floats on current
6. Ridicule
10. Uniform
11. Grain tips
12. Route
13. Skin irritation
14. Slight quarrel
15. Gloomy
16. For each one
17. Sums
18. Evaluate
19. Cooking herb
20. Terminated

Crossword 193

ACROSS
1. Shiny metal alloy
5. Hair parasites
7. Deem
8. Part of foot
9. Sport
10. Wooden packing case
11. Outlaw
13. Head support
14. Bicycle for two
18. Painting stands
21. Bluefin fish
22. Lack of interest
24. Military first-aid attendant
25. Blocking vote
26. Harness (oxen)
27. Sister's girl
28. Looked at warily
29. Dress ribbons

DOWN
1. Share house
2. Leered at
3. Cast out
4. Progress
5. Myths
6. Funny
12. Frozen water
15. Intensely
16. Clear gemstone
17. Interferes
19. Swiss mountain
20. Bashfulness
22. Land measures
23. Chasm

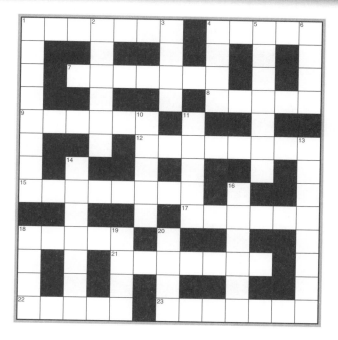

ACROSS
1. Gracefully stylish
4. Fundamental
7. Diabetic's preparation
8. Male duck
9. Return to custody
12. Resurface
15. Trainees
17. Allow
18. Tropical fruit
21. Envisage
22. Fights with fists
23. Obvious

DOWN
1. Outward
2. Amiable
3. Floor slate
4. 007 agent, James ...
5. Geometric shapes
6. Manage
10. Less wet
11. Make happen
13. Applicable
14. Self-contradictory statement
16. Sun-browned
18. Insincere (of speech)
19. Plans
20. Baked treat

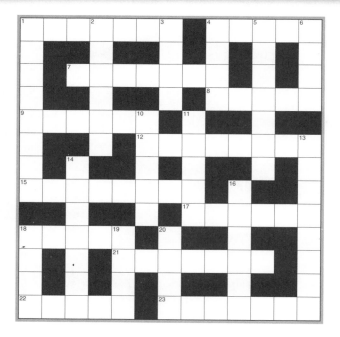

ACROSS
1. Petty objection
4. Sedate
7. Claimed
8. Apportion
9. Summoned
12. Reply
15. Waterside
17. Beat (corn)
18. Vibrate
21. Full of energy
22. Solitary person
23. Slid

DOWN
1. Satisfies (thirst)
2. Bravely
3. Brink
4. Soap foam
5. Gets
6. Take nap

10. Salivate
11. Small isle
13. Expressed
    keenness (over)
14. Abode on wheels
16. Hummed tunelessly
18. Blues/gospel
    music style
19. At all times
20. Wanes

ACROSS
1. Fiction books
5. Dry with cloth
7. Father's brother
8. Part of arrow
9. Sport squad
10. Instruct
11. Large migration
13. Make (profit)
14. Skill
18. Sprinted
21. Rein in

22. Principles
24. Proposition
25. Observe
26. Region
27. Banishment
28. Fix
29. Speckled

DOWN
1. Finest
2. Receded
3. Tailored ensembles

4. Grated
5. Moisture
6. Rolling grassland
12. Grecian pot
15. Rude
16. Jostled
17. Vehicular flow
19. As well as
20. Throw out
22. Peeved
23. Precise

Crossword 197

ACROSS
1. Bit persistently
5. Facial features
7. Prepared
8. Wearing footwear
9. Unclothed
10. Of sound
11. Lodges firmly
13. Successor
14. Gravies
18. Pattern
21. Roasting appliance
22. Pressed (clothes)
24. Track vehicle
25. Factual
26. Half
27. Innocent
28. Be introduced to
29. Gauging worth of

DOWN
1. Rubber seals
2. Thick slice
3. Frock
4. Goaded
5. Hangs unlawfully
6. Wadding
12. Female rabbit
15. Negative (criticism)
16. Happy
17. Filthy
19. Make mistake
20. Bobbing head
22. Surmise
23. Beginning

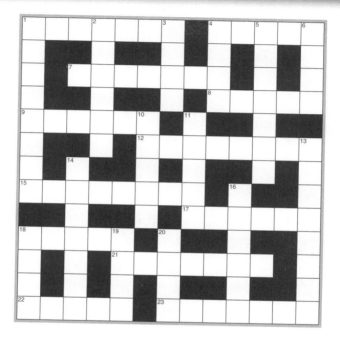

ACROSS
1. Beef cut
4. Avoid (capture)
7. Of fired clay
8. Cardiac organ
9. Risk
12. Curiosity
15. Drawings
17. Treated successfully
18. Lodge deeply
21. Encroachments
22. Witch's hex
23. Emitting

DOWN
1. Flock minder
2. Margin of safety
3. Without sensation
4. Inscribe
5. Map books
6. Opposite of west
10. Female opera singers
11. Hidden supply
13. Falling heavily
14. Leaf vegetable
16. Glorified
18. Shady trees
19. Aromatic herb
20. Factual

Crossword 199

ACROSS

1. Mythical stories
5. Chest wall bones
7. Exaggeratedly masculine
8. Molecule particle
9. Jump high
10. Freeze
11. Unlatch
13. Single object
14. Carnivores, meat ...
18. Four score
21. Cut with scissors
22. Universal
24. Reflection
25. Layer
26. Courageous man
27. Smooths
28. Tints
29. Ousts

DOWN

1. Key attraction
2. Suspended state
3. Artist's coat
4. Moon's obscuring of the sun
5. Throwing (dice)
6. Most valiant
12. Aggressive dog
15. Yearly stipend
16. Imperial realms
17. Smudged
19. Sick
20. Golden hues
22. Flying fowls
23. Earthy pigment

ACROSS

1. Legally kill
4. Emerge (of new chick)
7. Fire from job
8. Detected sound
9. For each, per ...
12. Mimes
15. Submissiveness
17. Shocking ordeal
18. Skewered meat dish
21. Drank
22. Not hollow
23. Survived

DOWN

1. Expulsion of evil spirits
2. Medical rooms
3. Lengthy movie
4. Peace & quiet
5. In direction of
6. Weeded
10. Felt pain
11. Midriff
13. Discarded
14. Women's court sport
16. Tiers
18. Young goats
19. Flying animal
20. Woodwind instrument

Crossword 201

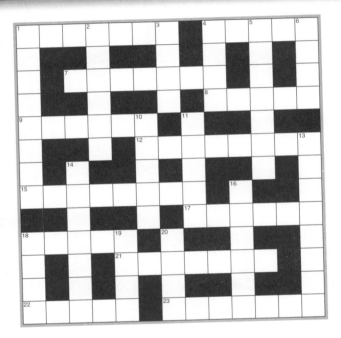

ACROSS
1. Journeyed
4. Sounded like crow
7. Side-by-side
8. Garden tool
9. Wrote name
12. Twisted forcibly
15. Trickled
17. Desires greatly
18. Call on socially
21. Attained
22. Open to view
23. Not inside

DOWN
1. Disappeared
2. Pure white animal
3. Sketch
4. Small beds
5. Floral memorial rings
6. ... & duchess
10. Resided
11. On standby
13. Deter
14. Crack
16. Fabricators
18. Blocking vote
19. Horse's gait
20. Kind of palm

ACROSS

1. Formal arguments
4. Hot water burn
7. Invoice
8. Sober
9. Smoothed (wood)
12. Speeches
15. Rush headlong (of herd)
17. Subtle shade of meaning
18. Discharged gun
21. Unstable
22. Bears in mind
23. Scribbled absent-mindedly

DOWN

1. Syrian capital
2. Shopping corridor
3. Spurn
4. Congeals
5. Pilot
6. Action
10. Gives medicine to
11. Consumed
13. Yelled
14. String-knotting art
16. Barred
18. Marine creature
19. Adds soundtrack to
20. Took advantage of

Crossword **203**

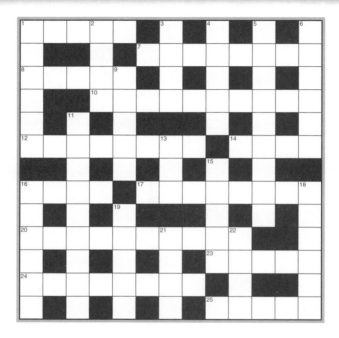

ACROSS
1. Book of maps
7. Speechmakers
8. From the time that
10. Very tall building
12. Lately
14. Brief calm
16. Quantity of paper
17. Deeply shocked
20. Evil conduct
23. Chaos
24. Most in want
25. Slalom competitor

DOWN
1. Reply
2. Circle curves
3. Therapeutic baths
4. Unite in matrimony
5. Usefully
6. Celestial
9. Just managing, ... out a living
11. Superficial cuts
13. Remove branches from
15. Low wetland
16. Using oars
18. Ballerina
19. Be appropriate to
21. Plane tip
22. Became submerged

ACROSS
1. Disapproves of
5. Capsize, ... over
7. Was indebted to
8. Mentally conjures up
9. Subtle difference
12. Pined
15. Requested from menu
19. Takes place
21. Keep apart
22. October birthstone
23. Conformed, ... the line
24. Edible fungus

DOWN
1. Asphyxiates in water
2. Heavily loaded
3. Cutting utensil
4. Beard trimmer
5. Chess horse
6. Secured with rope
10. Transfixed
11. Scorch
12. Short-lived trend
13. Long movie
14. Ballerina's skirt
15. Counterbalance
16. Small chore
17. Mummify
18. Psychiatric hospital
19. Premonitions
20. Singing group

Crossword **205**

ACROSS

1. Sorcerers
4. Australian marsupial
7. Results
8. Steam burn
9. Remove from danger
12. Railway bridges
15. Pulled a face
17. Radio interference
18. Playing-card Jack
21. Embarrassed
22. Levels
23. Showed gratitude to

DOWN

1. Irrigating
2. Influence
3. Footwear item
4. Touch lips
5. Move forward
6. Between
10. Eject from home
11. Exalts
13. Dotted
14. Wondrous thing
16. Cave chamber
18. Flying toy
19. Wheat tips
20. Breathe rapidly

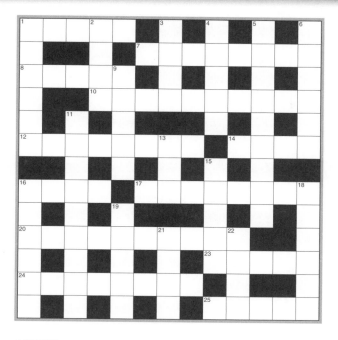

ACROSS
1. Russian liquor
7. Messier
8. Exchange
10. Moons
12. Hunt among refuse
14. Body's outer layer
16. Talk
17. Graceful style
20. Protective barriers
23. Soil
24. Allot
25. River mammal

DOWN
1. Ballot-casters
2. Young goats
3. AM, ... meridiem
4. Italian country house
5. Getting wrong
6. Correctional institution
9. Enthusiastic
11. Pleasant tasting
13. Clear toothpaste
15. Spry
16. French brandy
18. Any one of two
19. Authoritative order
21. Tiny insects
22. Common seasoning

Crossword **207**

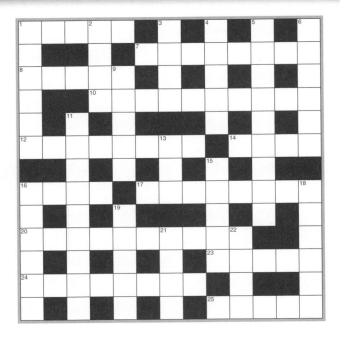

ACROSS
1. Sweetener
7. Seized (aircraft)
8. Adult girl
10. Self-reproach
12. Elegant
14. Arm
16. Grow dim
17. Below ocean's surface
20. Pillaging
23. Meant
24. Chosen
25. Slides

DOWN
1. Embroidering
2. A great distance
3. Number in quintet
4. Floating log platforms
5. Most slender
6. Verb modifier
9. On no occasion
11. Roman Catholic prelates
13. Grecian pot
15. Red dye
16. Wooded area
18. Dwellings
19. Whim
21. Bottom of boat
22. Fish breathing organ

ACROSS

1. Surpass in auction
5. Well ventilated
7. Very annoyed
8. Prompted (actor)
9. Authentic
10. Cowboy's rope
11. Eagerly
13. Cook in water
14. Delicate
18. Striding
21. Wound blemish
22. Rang (of bells)
24. Tough plastic
25. Unaccompanied
26. Mocking remark
27. Callous opportunists
28. Sight organs
29. African scavengers

DOWN

1. Fruit tree grove
2. Waited, ... one's time
3. Faintly
4. White root vegetable
5. Of heart/lung exercises
6. Reconfigure
12. Tennis call on serve
15. Small, salted fish
16. Anxious
17. More youthful
19. Affirmative vote
20. Mechanical devices
22. Luxurious & expensive
23. Journalist's slant

Crossword 209

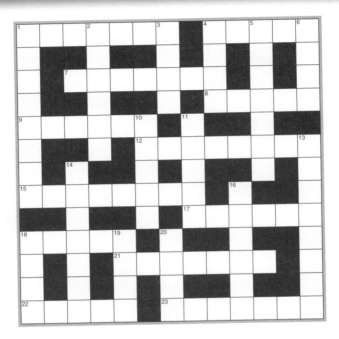

ACROSS

1. Stereo soundbox
4. Stage play
7. Surgical insert
8. Unadventurous
9. Scorched
12. Protruding part of cliff face
15. Rush headlong (of herd)
17. Radio interference
18. Cover with cloth
21. Sentence structure
22. Brave deeds
23. Eight-note intervals

DOWN

1. Flood-protection sacks
2. Supplying with guns
3. Paper quantity
4. Specks
5. Predictions year book
6. Very eager
10. Having a round roof
11. Relinquishes (territory)
13. Rivers of ice
14. Mosquito-borne fever
16. Yellow fruit
18. Unable to hear
19. Henhouse produce
20. Palm starch

Crossword 210

ACROSS

1. Of weddings
5. Bracing strut
7. Egg-producing organ
8. Bullock team harness
9. Close
10. Camera image
11. Sounds
13. Bobs head
14. Earmarked
18. Domesticating
21. Hat edge
22. More miserly
24. Reduce car speed
25. Election
26. Distribute playing cards
27. Heavy fencing swords
28. Performs slalom
29. Sings Swiss alpine-style

DOWN

1. Rifle knife
2. Rates
3. Circuits
4. Inherited British title
5. Like-meaning word
6. Leave (sinking ship)
12. Before (poetic)
15. Pipe-blocking bubble
16. Bets money
17. Smeared (reputation)
19. Top pilot
20. Foundation garments
22. Untidy
23. Contributed

Crossword 211

ACROSS
1. Roman M
5. Part of fish-hook
7. Chew like rat
8. Rekindle
9. Sidesteps
12. Imbiber
15. Transplanted (skin)
19. Carrion-eating animals
21. Entranceway chimes
22. Precious metal
23. Paved enclosure
24. International agreements

DOWN
1. Pulled sharply
2. Unmarried
3. Land units
4. Trader
5. Navigational warning light
6. Witty conversation
10. Sector
11. Way out
12. Unexploded shell
13. Very dark
14. Oven for pottery
15. Happily
16. Dreaded
17. Result
18. Stage whispers
19. Split in two
20. Number of spider's legs

Crossword 212

ACROSS
1. Big
7. Warm outer garment
8. Of the moon
10. Ricocheting
12. Exciting
14. Woe!
16. Witty remark
17. Of bone system
20. Overstate
23. Third planet
24. Wavered (on edge)
25. Not given food

DOWN
1. Soothed
2. Provoke
3. Elliptic
4. Batman's alter-ego, ... Wayne
5. Fashionable society person
6. Performance platforms
9. Of kidneys
11. Steered (course)
13. Rile
15. Woodwind instrument
16. Expeditions
18. Secured with rope
19. Leered at
21. Regretted
22. Gain

Crossword **213**

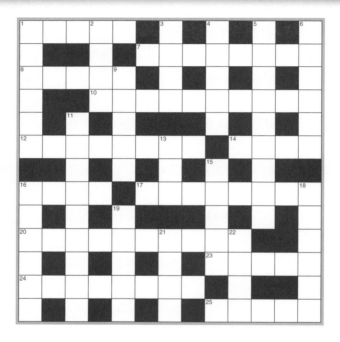

ACROSS
1. Trite
7. Escapees
8. Symbol
10. Deducted
12. Transplanting (skin)
14. The one here
16. Electrical unit
17. Heavy knives
20. Aroused again
23. Brazilian dance
24. Raises
25. Brown pigment

DOWN
1. Cutting with teeth
2. Inspires with reverence
3. Stalk prey
4. Long tales
5. Acrobatic movement
6. Incidental comments
9. Tasting of almonds or cashews
11. Room decor material
13. Zero
15. Destinies
16. Song parts
18. Musical composition
19. Tokyo is there
21. Viewed suspiciously
22. Stunned state

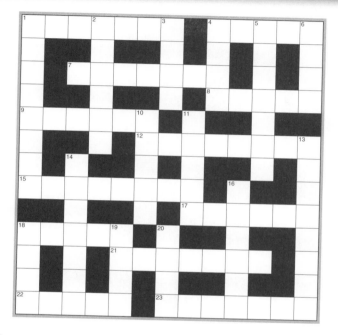

ACROSS

1. Floral memorial rings
4. Rub until sore
7. Property size
8. Camera light
9. Curiously coincidental
12. Trainees
15. Naval fleet task force
17. Cost-cutting efficiency
18. Cymbals sound
21. Standing on hind legs
22. Splashed (through)
23. Hindered

DOWN

1. Marriages
2. Regional speech pattern
3. Crash (into)
4. Kitchen professional
5. Clothing
6. Engrave
10. Office worker
11. Strands of threads
13. Imported illegally
14. Genetically altered
16. Even the score for
18. Glossy black bird
19. Network of lines
20. Indian garment

Crossword 215

ACROSS
1. Made cat sound
5. Pounce
7. Sad poem
8. Arm or leg
9. Pleasant
10. Ancient remnant
11. Anomaly
13. Owl's cry
14. Brutal
18. Unassuming
21. Spur
22. Complied with
24. Become informed
25. Very short skirt
26. Tablet
27. Light push
28. Male red deer
29. Rudder handle

DOWN
1. Bed headrests
2. Jewish scholar
3. Denounce
4. Recover (goods)
5. Hanged unlawfully
6. Mooring weights
12. Price ticket
15. Rescue by helicopter
16. Confounding
17. Enlarges
19. Globe
20. Walking infant
22. Beginning
23. Throw out

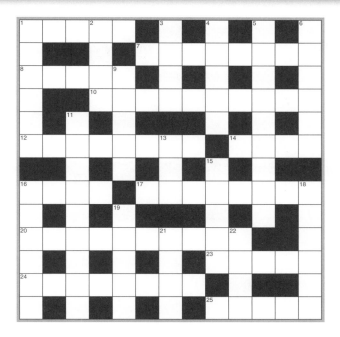

ACROSS
1. Duck's call
7. Increased in attractiveness
8. Edible innards
10. Tearing jaggedly
12. Negative consequence
14. Health resorts
16. Small island
17. Germ-free
20. Origins
23. Pulls sharply
24. Learns new job
25. Performed slalom

DOWN
1. Reported speech
2. Steam train fuel
3. One time only
4. Waterway
5. Being frugal
6. Wise sayings
9. Ewe's young
11. Windows over doors
13. Weep
15. Dirty-looking
16. Innate
18. Made to happen
19. Creep stealthily
21. Taverns
22. Became submerged

Crossword **217**

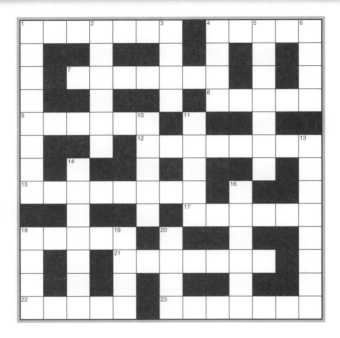

ACROSS
1. Found
4. Ahead of time
7. Stir
8. Speak slowly
9. Stared angrily
12. Most immature
15. Divergent lines
17. Emotional shock
18. Torment
21. Technical sketch
22. Literary style
23. Perspired

DOWN
1. Lawsuit contestant
2. Enrages
3. Tie in race
4. Viewed
5. Delighted
6. Shout
10. Perishing
11. Erupted
13. Foiled
14. Untouched (of meal)
16. Curved fruit
18. Tiny branch
19. Rim
20. Flying mammals

Crossword 218

ACROSS

1. Spanish fleet
5. Draw in (air)
7. Stale
8. Dingy
9. In the area of
10. Volley of bullets
11. Crowd brawls
13. Have (to)
14. Caught in the act
18. Entangle
21. Unnatural sleep
22. Library user
24. Actress, ... Kelly
25. Bully
26. Take nap
27. Happening
28. Electricity supply network
29. Moves furtively

DOWN

1. Stomach
2. Leisurely walk
3. Accumulate
4. Set apart
5. Like-meaning word
6. Meteor impact holes
12. Before (poetic)
15. One good turn deserves ...
16. Crowed
17. Formal arguments
19. Maiden name indicator
20. Horse restrainer
22. Hires out
23. Contributed

Crossword 219

ACROSS
1. Olive farms
5. Tumble
7. Metal rope
8. Necklace ball
9. Rock hollow
10. Huge
11. Personify
13. Outstanding loan
14. Scratch (surface)
18. Scatter
21. Verse writer
22. Mooring weight
24. Significant occurrence
25. Stupefy
26. Lost blood
27. Evil spirit
28. Embroiders
29. Effortlessly

DOWN
1. Wine cups
2. The V of DVD
3. Rough-skinned
4. Terminated
5. Ebbs
6. Habitable
12. Immerse
15. Snorting laugh
16. Is present at
17. Regards highly
19. Charged atom
20. Gruesomely
22. Make amends
23. Six-sided figures

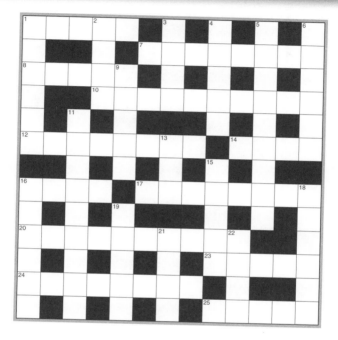

ACROSS
1. Solo vocal pieces
7. Puts (sword) in scabbard
8. Secrete
10. Arctic vehicle
12. Spanish treasure ships
14. Vending-machine aperture
16. Stack
17. Wrenched (ankle)
20. Midwifery
23. Detested
24. Angering
25. Near

DOWN
1. Growing old
2. Assists
3. Gnaw
4. Chaos
5. Exciting
6. State boldly
9. Walk through the door
11. Detergents
13. Crab's pinch
15. Eye cover
16. Animal feet
18. Dally
19. Meet & join
21. Talk wildly
22. Yacht canvas

Crossword 221

ACROSS
1. Precious metal
5. Yacht
7. Public persona
8. Enthusiastic devotion
9. Citrus tree
10. Tropical fruit
11. Mauve flowers
13. Drew
14. Stupefying
18. Military students
21. Uterus
22. Made airtight
24. Awkward
25. Clothing
26. Fencing sword
27. Fill with joy
28. Baron's title
29. Sprites

DOWN
1. Fried noisily
2. Italian country house
3. Circles
4. Extremist
5. Tardy
6. Side of chair
12. Tin container
15. Guacamole ingredient
16. Partook of alcohol
17. Entrance
19. Gorilla or chimpanzee
20. Jockeys' seats
22. Sheer
23. Fasten (to)

ACROSS

1. Money for good deed
5. Drinks slowly
7. Speak to crowd
8. Blowpipe missile
9. Adds (up)
10. Colossal
11. Christian place of worship
13. Eye membrane
14. UFO, flying ...
18. Tourist spots
21. Jog (memory)
22. Inbred
24. Plucked string sound
25. Garment worn in ancient Rome
26. As well
27. Verve
28. Early harp
29. Commands

DOWN

1. Lessens
2. Movie performer
3. Bread mixture
4. Plunders
5. Hardening
6. Loyal citizen
12. Snooker stick
15. Expression of regret
16. Small house
17. Become ill again
19. Tavern
20. Elders
22. Arctic shelter
23. Interweave

Crossword 223

ACROSS
1. Tile-chip picture
5. Cattle parasite
7. Reproductive organ
8. Front edge of tibia
9. July birthstone
10. Tropical fruit
11. Sick feeling
13. Must-have
14. Gaped tiredly
18. State of neglect
21. Dull
22. Halted
24. Sandy coast
25. Object of worship
26. Impartial
27. Finished
28. Betting chances
29. Funeral service speech

DOWN
1. Stonework craft
2. Mother's sisters
3. Latin American line dance
4. Coped
5. Cruel rulers
6. Spider traps
12. Night before
15. Worn by friction
16. Takes small bites
17. Forceful requests
19. Fury
20. Rather old
22. Reprimand
23. Dreadful

Solutions

1

```
L O C A T E   O   W I N G
O     B   J U R O R   E
Y O G A   E   G   O P A L
A     S C H A I N   R
L A T E S T   N   G L E E
T       U   I   E   S
Y A W N E D   C A D E T S
  N   E   I   R     L
T Y P E S   I C I C L E
  T   D I C E D   M   I
H I L L   U   O   P R I G
  M   E A S E L   E   H
K E Y S   S   S O L V E S
```

4

```
P O L A R   A   L   A   A
A   X   A B S O L V E D
T I B I A   L   O   O   V
R     S T R E A M L I N E
O   P   O   S     D   R
N E A R N E S S   L A M B
  R   E   E   C   N
Q U A Y   E X P L I C I T
U   M   A     A   E   R
E V E R G R E E N S   A
A   D   E   Y   S A V E D
S K I N N I E R   N   E
Y   C T   S   O G R E S
```

2

```
D O U B L I N G   T U R F
E   I   N   A   E   U
P L U G   C O M E D I E S
A   O   U   B   I   N
R E C T O R   L   U   I N
T   O G   T E E M I N G
  M   L   O   N   A
A C A D E M Y   T     A
N   A   E   V E T O E D
S   B   D I   I     M
W A R B L I N G   M I N I
E   E   U   I   E   T
R E E D   M E L O D I E S
```

5

```
M A C H I N E S   W O V E
O   O   O K H   S
G R U B   O R A T I O N S
U   O   K   T   T   A
L E A S E S   E E   Y
S   B   E   P R A N C E S
U   L   I   R   O
A R T I S A N   R   A
S   N   B   P A C K E D
T   B   A E   O   H
R E T R A C E D   M I T E
A   E   U A M   R
L E W D   S Y L L A B L E
```

3

```
P U T R I D   W   M I M E
A   A   A   E N E M Y   E
D Y E D   E A   S P A N
D   A   M E R I T S
L E A R N S   I   E E L S
E   I   N   R   E
D R I F T S   G A Y E S T
E   I   P   X     A
S L U R   E P E A L E D
I   E X C E L   R   P
T E E M   I   I   S U M O
V   A B A T E   O   L
M E A N   L   D E N U D E
```

6

```
H U S B A N D   R E F E R
A   E   E   A   L   O P
C   C H I E F L Y   O P
C A   Y   S P A C E
H U R L E D   A   T
I   F   I N D E C E N T
N D   G A   D   R U
G R A B B I N G   E N A C T S
  Z   T     R   U
G A Z E S   F   R   S T
I   L   E   R   F
S E A   W E A R I E S   E U
T E D D Y   E T E R N A L
```

Solutions

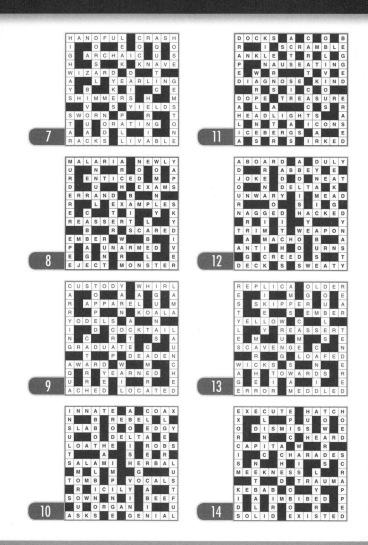

7

| | | | | | | | | | | | |
|H|A|N|D|F|U|L| |C|R|A|S|H|
|I| |O| |E| |O|Q| |O|
|G| |A|R|C|H|A|I|C| |U|S|
|H| |S| |K| |K|N|A|V|E|
|W|I|Z|A|R|D| |D| |T|
|A| |L| |Y|E|A|R|L|I|N|G|
|Y| |B| |K| |I| |C| |E|
S	H	I	M	M	E	R	S		H		M
	V		S		Y	I	E	L	D	S
S	W	O	R	N		P		R		T
T	U		O	R	A	T	I	N	G		O
A	A	D		L		I		I		N
R	A	C	K	S		L	I	V	A	B	L	E

11

DOCKS · A · C · O · B
R · I · SCRAMBLE
ANKLE · T · R · L · G
P · NAUSEATING · E
E · W · R · T · V · E
DIAGNOSE · KIND
R · S · I · C · O
DOPE · TREASURE
A · L · A · C · S · R
HEADLIGHTS · A
L · N · T · A · ICONS
ICEBERGS · A · E
A · S · R · S · IRKED

8

MALARIA · NEWLY
U · N · R · O · O · A
R · ENTICED · M · P
D · U · H · EXAMS
ERRAND · B · N
R · L · EXAMPLES
E · C · T · I · Y · K
REASSERT · L · Y
B · R · SCARED
EMBER · W · B · I
P · A · UNARMED · V
E · G · N · R · L · E
EJECT · MONSTER

12

ABOARD · A · DULY
D · R · ABBEY · E
JOKE · D · O · NEAT
O · N · DELTA · K
UNWARY · I · MEAD
R · O · S · I · G
NAGGED · HACKED
R · I · I · Y · Y
TRIM · T · WEAPON
A · MACHO · B · A
ANTI · H · O · URNS
G · CREED · S · T
DECK · S · SWEATY

9

CUSTODY · WHIRL
A · O · A · A · G · A
R · APPAREL · U · M
R · P · N · KOALA
YODELS · A · N
I · D · COCKTAIL
N · C · R · T · S · A
GRADUATE · C · U
T · P · DEADEN
AWARD · W · M · C
Q · R · YEARNED · H
U · R · E · I · R · E
ACHED · LOCATED

13

REPLICA · OLDER
E · I · M · G · O · E
S · SKIPPER · U · A
T · E · S · EMBER
YELLOW · C · L
L · Y · REASSERT
E · M · U · M · S · E
SCAVENGE · C · R
R · G · LOAFED
WICKS · S · N
A · H · TOWARDS · R
G · E · I · A · I · E
ERROR · MEDDLED

10

INNATE · A · COAX
N · B · REBEL · L
SLAB · O · O · EDGY
U · O · DELTA · E
LOATHE · I · ROBS
T · A · S · E · R
SALAMI · HERBAL
M · L · M · G · U
TOMB · P · VOCALS
R · ICILY · A · T
SOWN · N · I · BEEF
U · ORGAN · I · U
ASKS · E · GENIAL

14

EXECUTE · HATCH
X · L · P · U · O · O
O · DISMISS · W · E
R · N · C · HEARD
CAPITA · W · R
I · C · CHARADES
S · N · H · I · S · C
MEEKNESS · L · A
T · D · TRAUMA · P
KEBAB · O · Y · P
I · A · IMBIBED · E
D · L · R · O · R · E
SOLID · EXISTED

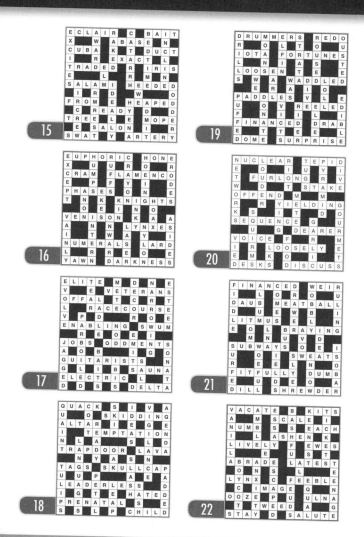

15

E	C	L	A	I	R		C		B	A	I	T
X			W		A	B	A	S	E		N	
C	U	B	A		K		T		D	U	C	T
I			R			E	X	A	C	T		L
T	R	A	D	E	D		R			I	R	I	S
E			L		R		M		N		
S	A	L	A	M	I		H	E	E	D	E	D
	I		R		D		W				
F	R	O	M		E		H	E	A	P	E	D
	C			R	E	A	D	Y		D		R
T	R	E	E		L		E		M	O	P	E
E			S	A	L	O	N		I			R
S	W	A	T		Y		A	R	T	E	R	Y

16

E	U	P	H	O	R	I	C		H	O	N	E
X		U		U		R		O		R	
C	R	A	M		F	L	A	M	E	N	C	O
E		P		F		Y		I			D	
P	H	A	S	E	S		O	N				D
T		N	K		K	N	I	G	H	T	S	
	O		E		I		N		O			
V	E	N	I	S	O	N		K		A	A	
A		N		N		L	Y	N	X	E	S	
I		T		W		A		Y		I		
N	U	M	E	R	A	L	S		L	A	R	D
L		R		R		R	E	K	O			E
Y	A	W	N		D	A	R	K	N	E	S	S

17

E	L	I	T	E		M		D		N		E
V		E			V	E	T	E	R	A	N	S
O	F	F	A	L		T		C		R		T
L			R	A	C	E	C	O	U	R	S	E
V		P		D		R		R		O		E
E	N	A	B	L	I	N	G		S	W	U	M
	R		E		O		E		I			
J	O	B	S		O	D	D	M	E	N	T	S
A	O		B		I		G			O		N
G	U	I	T	A	R	I	S	T	S			A
G	L			I		B		S	A	U	N	A
E	L	E	C	T	R	I	C		L		T	
D		D		S		S		D	E	L	T	A

18

Q	U	A	C	K		S	I	V		A	
U		O		S	K	I	D	D	I	N	G
A	L	T	A	R		I		E		G	E
I			T	E	M	P	T	A	T	I	O	N
N		L		A			S		L		D
T	R	A	P	D	O	O	R		L	A	V	A
	N		Y		A		S	N		
T	A	G	S		S	K	U	L	L	C	A	P
U		U		P		A		A		E	
L	E	A	D	E	R	L	E	S	S		D
I		G		T		E		H	A	T	E	D
P	R	E	N	A	T	A	L		S		E
S		S		L		P		C	H	I	L	D

19

D	R	U	M	M	E	R	S		R	E	D	O
R		O		L		T		O		U	
I	O	T	A		F	O	R	T	U	N	E	S
L			N		I		A		S		T	
L	O	O	S	E	N		T		A		E	
S		W		A		W	A	D	D	L	E	D
	E		R	A	I	O				O		
P	A	D	D	L	E	S		V		L	E	
U		O		V			R	E	E	L	E	D
F		N		E		L		I			L	
F	I	N	A	N	C	E	D		D	R	A	B
E		T		T		E		E			E	L
D	O	M	E		S	U	R	P	R	I	S	E

20

N	U	C	L	E	A	R		T	E	P	I	D
E		O		I		U		Y		I	
T		F	U	R	L	O	N	G		R	V	
W		O		D		T		S	T	A	K	E
O	F	F	E	N	D		M		M		
R		R		Y	I	E	L	D	I	N	G	
K		S		I		T		D			O	
S	E	Q	U	E	N	C	E		G			
	U			G			D	E	A	R	E	R
V	O	I	C	E		F		R		Y		M
I		R			L	O	O	S	E	L	Y	E
E		M		K	O		O			I		T
D	E	S	K	S		D	I	S	C	U	S	S

21

F	I	N	A	N	C	E	D		W	E	I	R
I		L		O		R		O		U	
D	A	U	B		M	E	A	T	B	A	L	L
D		U		E		W		B			I	
L	I	T	M	U	S		E	E	L		N	
E		O		L		B	R	A	Y	I	N	G
	M		N		U		V	D			
S	U	B	W	A	Y	S		O		E		I
U		O		I		S	W	E	A	T	S	
R		E		E		L		N			O	
F	I	T	F	U	L	L	Y		D	U	M	B
E			U	D		E		O			A	
D	I	L	L		S	H	R	E	W	D	E	R

22

V	A	C	A	T	E		B		K	I	T	S
A		M		S	C	A	L	E		I		
N	U	M	B		S		S		E	A	C	H
I		L		A	S	H	E	N		K		
L	I	V	E	L	Y		F		E	W	E	S
L		E			U		S		T		
A	B	R	A	D	E		L	A	T	E	S	T
	O		N			S		L			E	
L	Y	N	X		C		F	E	E	B	L	E
C		I	M	A	G	E		Q				N
O	O	Z	E		P		U	U	L	N	A	
T			T	W	E	E	D	A		A		G
S	T	A	Y		D		S	A	L	U	T	E

Solutions

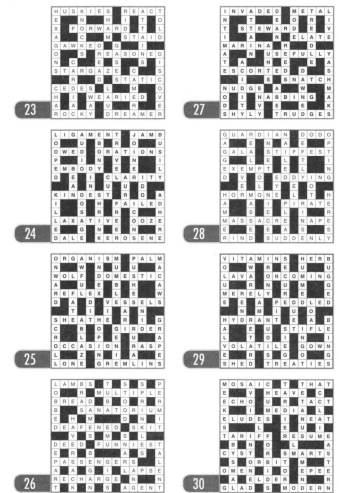

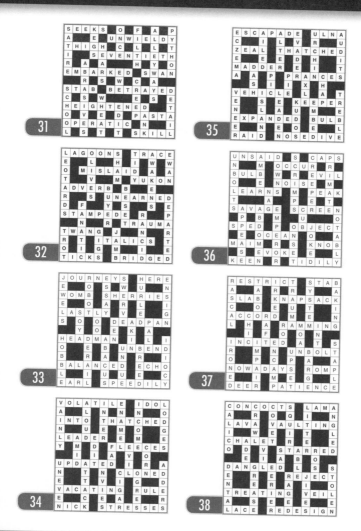

Solutions

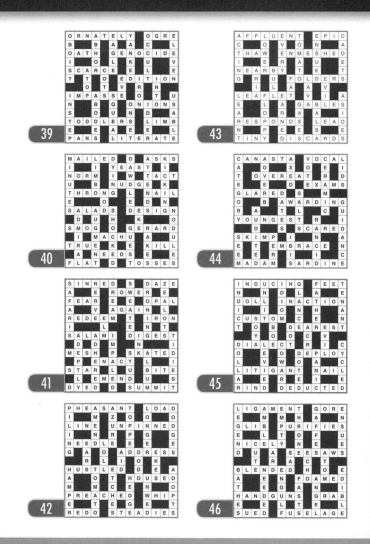

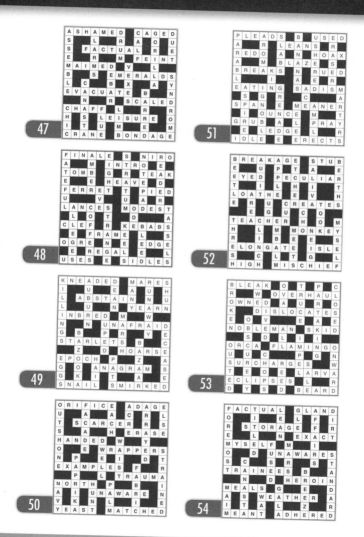

Solutions

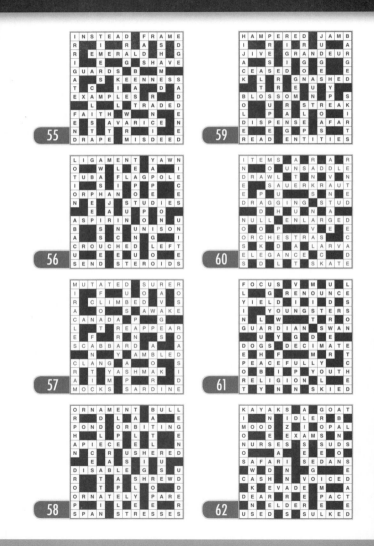

55

```
I N S T E A D   F R A M E
R   I   R   A   S   D
R   E M E R A L D   H   G
I   E   G   S H A V E   M
G U A R D S   B   M
A   S   K E E N N E S S
T   C   I   A   D   A
E X A M P L E S   R   D
E   L   L   T R A D E D
F A I T H   W   N   E
E   S   A V A R I C E   N
N   T   T   R   I   I
D R A P E   M I S D E E D
```

59

```
H A M P E R E D   J A M B
I   R   I   R   U   A
J I V E   G R A N D E U R
A   S   I   G   G   G
C E A S E D   O   R   E
K   L   R   G N A S H E D
  T   R   E   U   Y
B L O S S O M   N   P   S
O   U   R   S T R E A K
L   P   A   L   O   I
D I S P E N S E   A F A R
E   E   G   P   S   T
R E A D   E N T I T I E S
```

56

```
L I G A M E N T   Y A W N
O   W   L   E   A   I
T U B A   F L A G P O L E
I   S   I   P   P   C
O R P H A N   O   E   E
N   E   J   S T U D I E S
  A   U   P   O   O
A S P I R I N   O   N   U
B   S   N   U N I S O N
A   S   C   N   G   I
C R O U C H E D   L E F T
U   E   E   U   O   E
S E N D   S T E R O I D S
```

60

```
I T E M S   A   R   A   R
N   O   U N S A D D L E
D R A W L   T   N   V   N
E   P   S A U E R K R A U T
E   P   U   S   N   E
D R A G G I N G   S T U D
  D   H   U   N   A
N U L L   E N L A R G E D
O   O   P   V   E   E
O R C H E S T R A S   C
S   K   D   A   L A R V A
E L E G A N C E   C   D
S   D   L   T   S K A T E
```

57

```
M U T A T E D   S U R E R
I   F   U   O   A   O
R   C L I M B E D   V   S
A   O   S   A W A K E
C A N A D A   P   G
L   T   R E A P P E A R
E   F   R   N   S   O
S C A B B A R D   A   A
  N   Y   A M B L E D
C L A N G   A   O   S
R   T   Y A S H M A K   I
A   I   M   P   R   D
M O C K S   S A R D I N E
```

61

```
F O C U S   V   M   U   L
L   G   R E N O U N C E
Y I E L D   I   I   D   S
I   Y O U N G S T E R S
N   L   W   T   R   O
G U A R D I A N   S W A N
  U   Y   G   D   E
D O G S   D E C I M A T E
E   H   F   M   R   T
P E A C E F U L L Y   C
O   B   I   P   Y O U T H
R E L I G I O N   L   E
T   Y   N   N   S K I E D
```

58

```
O R N A M E N T   B U L L
R   D   L   A   A   E
P O N D   O R B I T I N G
H   L   P   L   T   E
A P I E C E   E   L   N
N   C   R   U S H E R E D
  E   A   S   I   U
D I S A B L E   G   S U
R   T   A   S H R E W D
O   T   P   L   O   D
O R N A T E L Y   P A R E
P   I   L   E   E   R
S P A N   S T R E S S E S
```

62

```
K A Y A K S   A   G O A T
I   N   I D L E R   B
M O O D Z   I   O P A L
O   E   E X A M S   N
N U R S E S   S   S U D S
O   A   E   E   O
S A F A R I   S E D A N S
  W   D   N   G   E
C A S H   N   V O I C E D
K   E V A D E   M   A
D E A R   R   E   P A C T
N   E L D E R   E   E
U S E D   S   S U L K E D
```

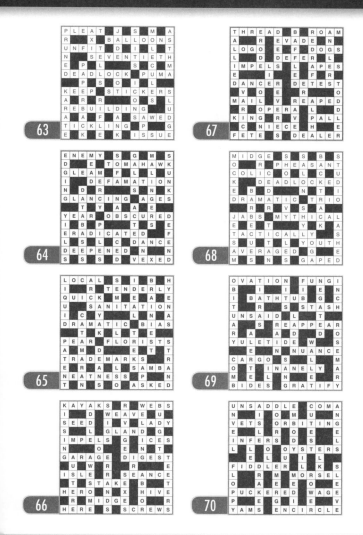

Solutions

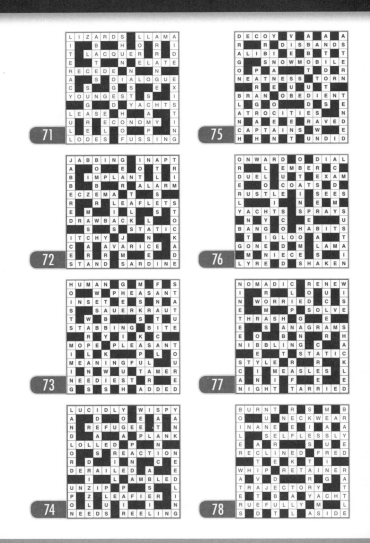

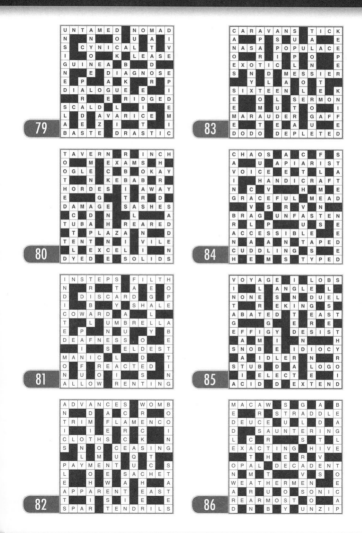

79

```
U N T A M E D     N O M A D
N     N     O     U   A     I
S   C Y N I C A L     T     V
I     O     K     L E A S E
G U I N E A     B     D
N     E     D I A G N O S E
E     P     A     K     R     P
D I A L O G U E     E     I
    R     E     R I D G E D
S C A L D     L     I     E
L     A V A R I C E     M
A     E     Z     I     T     I
B A S T E     D R A S T I C
```

80

```
T A V E R N     R     I N C H
O     M     E X A M S     H
O G L E     C     B     O K A Y
T     N     K E B A B     R
H O R D E S     I     A W A Y
E     G     T     R     D
D A M A G E     S A S H E S
    C     D     N     L     A
T U B A     H     R E A R E D
T     P L A Z A     N     D
T E N T     N     I     V I L E
L     E X C E L     I     N
D Y E D     E     S O L I D S
```

81

```
I N S T E P S     F I L T H
N     R     T     A     E     O
D     D I S C A R D     G     P
I     B     Y     S H A L E
C O W A R D     A     L
T     E     L     U M B R E L L A
E     P     N     U     Y     B
D E A F N E S S     O     E
    I     S     E L D E S T
M A N I C     L     D     I
O     F     R E A C T E D     N
N     U     O     I     S     N
A L L O W     R E N T I N G
```

82

```
A D V A N C E S     W O M B
N     D     A     C     R     O
T R I M     F L A M E N C O
I     I     E     R     C     I
C L O T H S     C     K     N
S     N     O     C E A S I N G
L     M     U     Q     T
P A Y M E N T     U     C     S
L     O     E     S A C H E T
E     H W A     H     A     A
A P P A R E N T     E A S T
T     I     S     I     E     E
S P A R     T E N D R I L S
```

83

```
C A R A V A N S     T I C K
A     P     S     U     A     E
N A S A     P O P U L A C E
O     R     I     P     O     P
E X O T I C     L     N     E
S     N     D     M E S S I E R
    Y     L     A     O     T
S I X T E E N     L     E     K
E     O     L     S E R M O N
E     M     U     T     O     I
M A R A U D E R     G A F F
E     T     E     A     U     E
D O D O     D E P L E T E D
```

84

```
C H A O S     A     C     F     S
A     U     A P I A R I S T
V O I C E     T     L     A
I     H A N D I C R A F T
N     C     V     H     M     E
G R A C E F U L     M E A D
    V     S     R     V     N
B R A G     U N F A S T E N
R     L     P     U     S     E
A C C E S S I B L E     S
N     A     A     N     T A P E D
C U D D L I N G     S     E
H     E     M     S     T Y P E D
```

85

```
V O Y A G E     I     L O B S
I     L     A N G L E     L     A
N O N E     S     N     D U E L
T     R     E K I N G     S
A B A T E D     T     E A S T
G     G     G     E     R     E
E F F I G Y     D E S I S T
A     M     I     N     H
S N O B     E     I D I O C Y
A     I D L E R     N     R
S T U B     D     A     L O G O
I     E L E C T     E     I
A C I D     D     E X T E N D
```

86

```
M A C A W     S     G     A     B
E     R     S T R A D D L E
D E U C E     U     L     D     A
D     S A U N T E R I N G
L     C     R     S     T     L
E X A C T I N G     H I V E
    T     H     E     R     V
O P A L     D E C A D E N T
N     M     T     V     S     O
W E A T H E R M E N     E
A     R     U     O     S O N I C
R E A R M O S T     O     A
D     N     B     Y     U N Z I P
```

Solutions

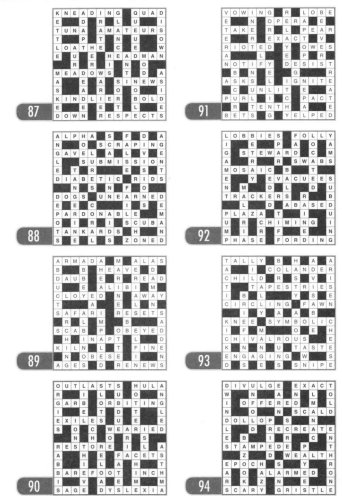

87

88

89

90

91

92

93

94

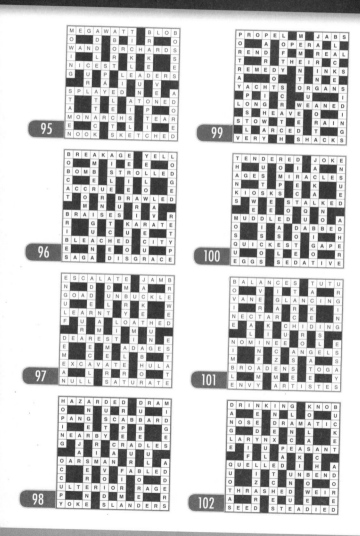

95 96 97 98 99 100 101 102

Solutions

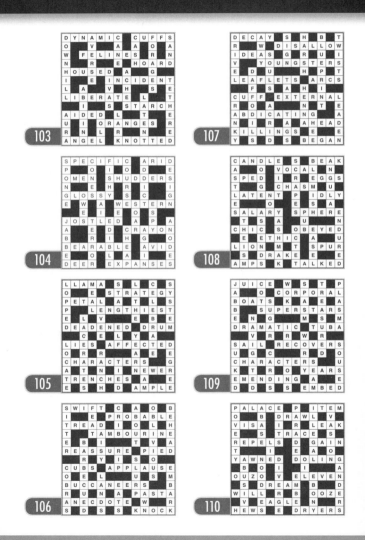

103

104

105

106

107

108

109

110

Solutions

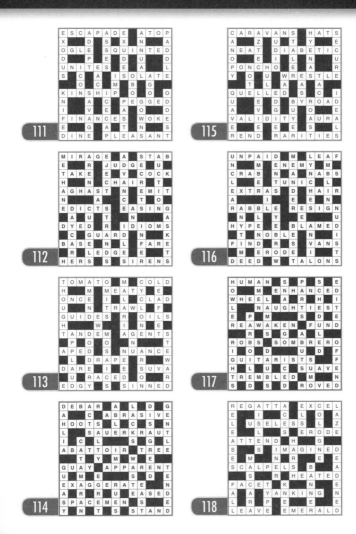

111
```
E S C A P A D E   A T O P
X     D   S   X   N     A
O G L E   S Q U I N T E D
D     P   E   D   U   D
U N I T E S   E   A     L
S     C A   I S O L A T E
      O   C   M   B   G
K I N S H I P   O   O   O
N     A   C   P E G G E D
I     V   E   A   O   D
F I N A N C E S   W O K E
E     G   A   T   N     S
D I N E   P L E A S A N T
```

112
```
M I R A G E   A   S T A B
E     R   J U D G E   U
T A K E   E   V   C O C K
H     N   C H A I R   T
A G H A S T   N   E M I T
N     A   A   C   T   O
E D I C T S   E A S I N G
A     U   T   N   A   A
D Y E D   R   I D I O M S
C     G U A R D   N   K
B A S E   N   L   F A R E
R     L E D G E   E   T
H E R S   S   S I R E N S
```

113
```
T O M A T O   M   C O L D
H     M   M E A T Y   E
O N C E   I   L   C L A D
U     N   T R A W L   F
G U I D E S   R   O I L S
H     W   I   N   E
T A N D E M   A G E N T S
P     O   O   N   T
A P E D   S   N U A N C E
L     D R A P E   R   W
D A R E   I   E   S U V A
U     R A C E D   O   R
E D G Y   S   S I N N E D
```

114
```
D E B A R   A   L   D   G
A     C   A B R A S I V E
H O O T S   L   C   S   N
L     I   S A U E R K R A U T
I   C   L     S   G   L
A B A T T O I R   T R E E
    T   Y   M   W   E
Q U A Y   A P P A R E N T
U     M   E     S   D   E
E X A G G E R A T E     N
A     R   R   U   E A S E D
S P A C E M E N   S     E
Y     N   T   S   S T A N D
```

115
```
C A R A V A N S   H A T S
A     Z   U   T   Y     E
N E A T   D I A B E T I C
O     E   I   L   N     U
P O N C H O   E   E   A R
Y     O   U   W R E S T L E
      T   L   A   A   A
Q U E L L E D   S   C   I
U     E   D   B Y R O A D
A     V   G   U   O   E
V A L I D I T Y   A U R A
E     E   E   E   S     L
R E N D   R A R I T I E S
```

116
```
U N P A I D   M   L E A F
N     M   E N E M Y   M
C R A B   N   A   N A B S
L     E   T U N I C   L
E X T R A S   D   H A I R
A     A   I   E   E   N
R A B B L E   R E S I G N
N     L   Y   E   U
H Y P E   E   B L A M E D
T     N O B L E   N   I
F I N D   R   S   V A N S
M     E R O D E   I   T
D E E D   W   T A L O N S
```

117
```
H U M A N   S   P   S E
O     M   E N H A N C E D
W H E E L   A   R   H I
L     N A U G H T I E S T
E P M     S   D   E
R E A W A K E N   F U N D
    R   S   G   A   L
R O B S   S O M B R E R O
I     O   D   U   D   F
G U I T A R I S T S     F
H     L   U   C   S U A V E
T R E M B L E D   M     N
S     D   S   D   R O V E D
```

118
```
R E G A T T A   E X C E L
E     I   C   L   O     A
L   U S E L E S S   L   Z
E     L   S   S   E R O D E
A T T E N D   H   E
S     S   I M A G I N E D
E M   M   N   R   E     A
S C A L P E L S   B     A
      R   H E A T E D
F A C E T   K   N     E
A     A   Y A N K I N G
L     R   P   E   E     N
L E A V E   E M E R A L D
```

Solutions

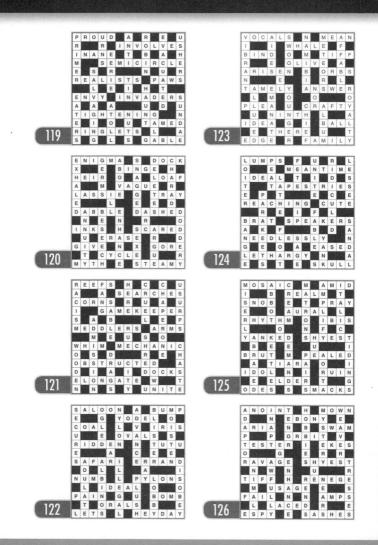

119
120
121
122
123
124
125
126

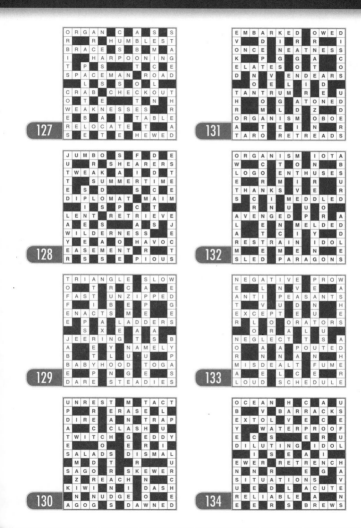

127

128

129

130

131

132

133

134

Solutions

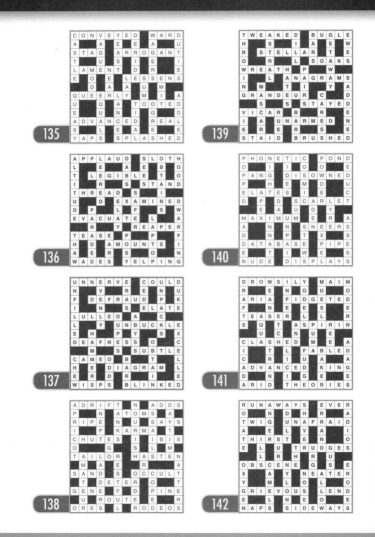

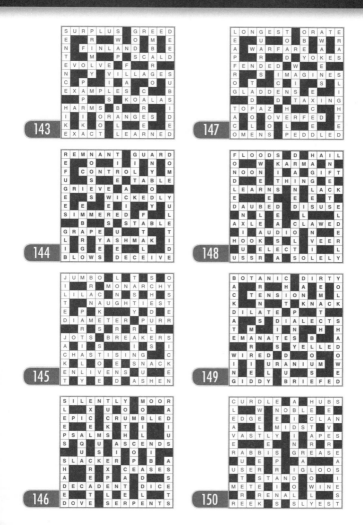

143

S	U	R	P	L	U	S			G	R	E	E	D	
E		R			W	O		M		E				
N		F	I	N	L	A	N	D		B		E		
T		M			P		S	C	A	L	D			
E	V	O	L	V	E		F			R				
N		Y		V	I	L	L	A	G	E	S			
C		P		I		A		O		U		B		
E	X	A	M	P	L	E	S		C			U		
L		P				S		K	O	A	L	A	S	
H	A	R	M	S		B		R		R		I		
L		I		O	R	A	N	G	E	S	D			
K		K		L		E		E		E				
E	X	A	C	T			L	E	A	R	N	E	D	

147

L	O	N	G	E	S	T		O	R	A	T	E	
E		U		O		B		W		R			
A		W	A	R	F	A	R	E		A		R	
P		R		D		Y	O	K	E	S			
F	E	N	D	E	D		W			E			
R		S		I	M	A	G	I	N	E	S		
O		T		C		I		S		L			
G	L	A	D	D	E	N	S	E		E		H	
		D		D		T	A	X	I	N	G		
T	O	P	A	Z		H		C				C	
A		O			O	V	E	R	F	E	D		
C		L		O		L		E				E	
O	M	E	N	S			P	E	D	D	L	E	D

144

R	E	M	N	A	N	T			G	U	A	R	D	
E		O		I		I		N		O				
F		C	O	N	T	R	O	L		Y		M		
U		S		E			T	A	B	L	E			
G	R	I	E	V	E			A		O				
E		E		S		W	I	C	K	E	D	L	Y	
E		E			E		I		Y		U			
S	I	M	M	E	R	E	D		F		L			
		B		S		S		S	T	A	B	L	E	
G	R	A	P	E		U		T		T				
L		R		Y	A	S	H	M	A	K		I		
I		G		E		E		L		L		D		
B	L	O	W	S			D	E	C	E	I	V	E	

148

F	L	O	O	D	S		D			H	A	I	L
O		W		K	A	R	M	A		N			
N	O	O	N		I		A		G	I	F	T	
D		E		T	H	I	N	G		E			
L	E	A	R	N	S			N		L	A	C	K
E		E			E		E	T					
D	A	U	B	E	D		D	I	S	U	S	E	
N		L		E		L		L					
A	X	L	E		A		C	L	A	W	E	D	
I		A	U	D	I	O		N					
H	O	O	K		S		L		V	E	E	R	
U		E	L	E	C	T		I				L	
U	S	S	R		A			S	O	L	E	L	Y

145

J	U	M	B	O		L		T		S		O	
I		R		M	O	N	A	R	C	H	Y		
L	I	L	A	C		N		S		H		S	
T		N	A	U	G	H	T	I	E	S	T		
E		P		K		Y		D		E			
D	I	A	M	E	T	E	R		P	U	R	R	
		R		S		R		L					
J	O	T	S		B	R	E	A	K	E	R	S	
A		I		S		I		S		I		
C	H	A	S	T	I	S	I	N	G			C	
K		L		O		E		S	N	A	C	K	
E	N	L	I	V	E	N	S		U			E	
T		Y		E		D		A	S	H	E	N	

149

B	O	T	A	N	I	C		D	I	R	T	Y	
A		R		H		A		E		O			
C		T	E	N	S	I	O	N		M	L		
K		N		T		K	N	A	C	K			
D	I	L	A	T	E		P		T				
A		S		D	I	A	L	E	C	T	S		
T		M		I		N		H					
E	M	A	N	A	T	E	S		B		A		
		R		S			Y	E	L	L	E	D	
W	I	R	E	D		D			O		O		
I		I		U	R	A	N	I	U	M		W	
N		E		L		U			S			E	
G	I	D	D	Y			B	R	I	E	F	E	D

146

S	I	L	E	N	T	L	Y			M	O	O	R
L		X		U		O		M		O			A
E	P	I	C		C	R	U	M	B	L	E	D	
E				K		T		I		I			
P	S	A	L	M	S		H	C		L		U	
S		Q		U		A	S	C	E	N	D	S	
		U		S		I		O		I			
S	L	A	C	K	E	R		P		B		A	
H		R		X		C	E	A	S	E	S		
A		E		P		A		D		S			
D	E	C	A	D	E	N	T		D	I	C	E	
E		T		L		E		L		T			
D	O	V	E			S	E	R	P	E	N	T	S

150

C	U	R	D	L	E		A			H	U	B	S
L			W		N	O	B	L	E			E	
E	D	G	E		E		I			C	L	A	N
A			L		M	I	D	S	T			V	
V	A	S	T	L	Y		I			A	P	E	S
E				E		N		R		R			
R	A	B	B	I	S		G	R	E	A	S	E	
		U			E					A			A
U	S	E	R			R		I	G	L	O	O	S
		T		S	T	A	N	D		O			I
M	E	T	E		I		O		W	I	N	E	
		R		R	E	N	A	L					
R	E	E	K		S			S	L	Y	E	S	T

Solutions

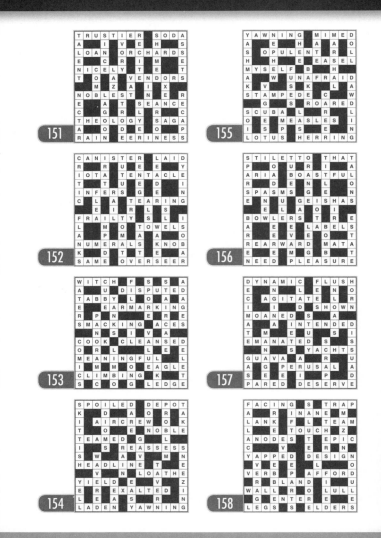

151

TRUSTIER · SODA
LOAN · ORCHARDS
NICELY · VENDORS
NOBLEST · SEANCE
THEOLOGY · SAGA
RAIN · EERINESS

152

CANISTER · LAID
IOTA · TENTACLE
INFERS · TEARING
FRAILTY · TOWELS
NUMERALS · KNOB
SAME · OVERSEER

153

WITCH · DISPUTED
TABBY · EARMARKING
SMACKING · ACES
COOK · CLEANSED
MEANINGFUL
CLIMBING · EAGLE
LEDGE

154

SPOILED · DEPOT
AIRCREW · NOBLE
TEAMED · REASSESS
HEADLINE · LOATHE
YIELD · EXALTED
LADEN · YAWNING

155

YAWNING · MIMED
OPULENT · EASEL
MYSELF · UNAFRAID
STAMPEDE · ROARED
SCUBA · MEASLES
LOTUS · HERRING

156

STILETTO · THAT
ARIA · BOASTFUL
SPASMS · GEISHAS
BOWLERS · LABELS
REARWARD · MATA
NEED · PLEASURE

157

DYNAMIC · FLUSH
AGITATE · SHOWN
MOANED · INTENDED
EMANATED · YACHTS
GUAVA · PERUSAL
PARED · DESERVE

158

FACING · TRAP
LANK · INANE · TEAM
TOUCH
ANODES · EPIC
YAPPED · DESIGN
VERB · AFFORD
BLAND
WALL · LULL
ENTER
LEGS · ELDERS

Solutions

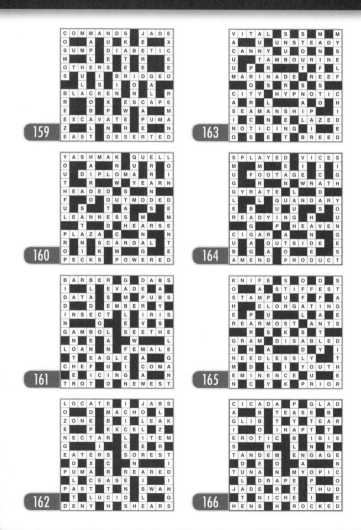

159

```
C O M M A N D S    J A D E
O    A   U   K   E      X
S U M P   D I A B E T I C
M    L   E   T   R      E
O T H E R S   E   E      E
S    U   I   B R I D G E D
     L   S   I   O   A
B L A C K E N   N   L   R
R    O   X   E S C A P E
E    B   P   W   A      M
E X C A V A T E   P U M A
Z    L   N   R   E      N
E A S T   D E S E R T E D
```

163

```
V I T A L   S   S   M   M
A    U   U N S T E A D Y
C A N N Y   U   O   N   S
U    U   T A M B O U R I N E
U    P   R   T   F      I
M A R I N A D E   R E E F
     O   S   R   S      S
C I T Y   H Y P N O T I C
A    R   L   A   O      H
S E A M A N S H I P      I
U    N   E   L A Z E D   P
N O T I C I N G   I      E
O    S   E T   B R E E D
```

160

```
Y A S H M A K   Q U E L L
O    A   M   N   U   R   O
U   D I P L O M A   R   I
T    R   W   Y E A R N
H E A D E D   S   N
U    S   O   O U T M O D E D
S    T   A   S   E      E
L E A N N E S S   M      M
     T   D   H E A R S E
P L A Z A   C   N   N   N
R    N   S C A N D A L   T
O    I   K   M   G      E
P E C K S   P O W E R E D
```

164

```
S P L A Y E D   V I C E S
M    M   E   I   I      G
U   F O O T A G E   C   G
G    R   N   W R A T H
G Y R A T E   L   D
L    L   Q U A N D A R Y
E    E   U   U   S   O
R E A D Y I N G   H      U
     G   P   H E A V E N
C I G A R   A   N      S
U    A   O U T S I D E   E
B   G   A   O   E      S
A M E N D   P R O D U C T
```

161

```
B A R B E R   G   D A B S
I    L   E V A D E   A
D A T A S   M   P U B S
D    D   E M B E R   Y
I N S E C T   L   I R I S
N    O   E   V   S
G A M B O L   S E E T H E
N    E   A   W      L
L O A N   N   F E M A L E
T    E A G L E   A   G
C H E F   U   I   C O M A
E    I C I N G   A   N
T R O T   D   N E W E S T
```

165

```
K N I F E   S   O   D   S
O    A   S T I F F E S T
S T A M P   U   F   F   A
H    E   E L O N G A T I N G
E    P   U   L   A      E
R E A R M O S T   A N T S
R    S   K   S   T
G R A M   D I S A B L E D
U    M   A   D   Y      I
N E E D L E S S L Y      T
M    D   L   I   Y O U T H
E M I N E N C E   U      E
N    C   Y   K   P R I O R
```

162

```
L O C A T E   I   J A B S
O    D   M A C H O   L
Z O N E   B   I   L E A K
E    P   E X C E L   Z
N E C T A R   L   I T E M
G    I   E   E   R
E A T E R S   S O R E S T
     D   X   C   N      I
P U M A   R E A R E D
     L   C E A S E   I   I
P A S T   T   N   S W A N
T    L U C I D   L      G
D E N Y   H   S H E A R S
```

166

```
C I C A D A   P   G L A D
A    B   T E A S E   B
G L I B   T   Y   T E A R
I    O   I N A P T   T
E R O T I C   B   I B I S
S    R   E   R   N      N
T A N D E M   E N G A G E
D    E   O   A      N
T U N A   M Y O P I C
L    D R A P E   P      N
J A D E   R   T   T H U D
T    N I C H E   I      E
H E N S   H   R O C K E D
```

Solutions

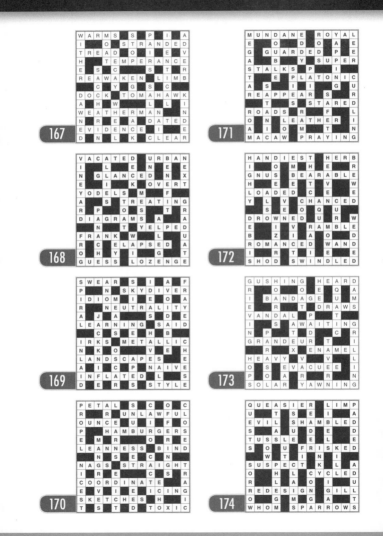

167

```
W A R M S     S   P   I     A
I       O   S T R A N D E D
T R E A D   O   I   E     V
H     T E M P E R A N C E   R
E   S C     S   T     S   R
R E A W A K E N     L I M B
  C   Y   G   S   C
D O C K   T O M A H A W K
A   H   W     L   L   I
W E A T H E R M A N     I
N   R   E   A   D A T E D
E V I D E N C E     I     E
D   N   L   K   C L E A R
```

171

```
M U N D A N E     R O Y A L
E     O     D O   A     E
G   G U A R D E D   P   E
A   B     Y   S U P E R
S T A L K S   P   I
T   E     P L A T O N I C
A   S   I   I     G   U
R E A P P E A R   S     R
  R   T   S   S T A R E D
R O A D S   R     F     L
O   N   L E A T H E R   I
A   I   O     M     T   N
M A C A W     P R A Y I N G
```

168

```
V A C A T E D     U R B A N
I   L     E   N   E   E
N   G L A N C E D   N   X
E   I     K   O V E R T
Y O D E L S   M     F
A   S     T R E A T I N G
R   P     O   S   T   R
D I A G R A M S   A   A
R   N   T   Y E L P E D
F R A N K   W     L   U
R   C   E L A P S E D   A
O   H   Y   I     G   T
G U E S S     L O Z E N G E
```

172

```
H A N D I E S T     H E R B
I     O   M   H   E     R
G N U S   B E A R A B L E
H   E   E   T   V     W
L O A D E D   C   E   E
Y   L   V   C H A N C E D
    S   E   O   Q   U
D R O W N E D   U   R   W
E   I   I V   R A M B L E
B   Z   I   A   O   D
R O M A N C E D   W A N D
I   R   T   I     E   E
S H O D     S W I N D L E D
```

169

```
S W E A R     S   I   A   F
P   N   S K Y D I V E R
I D I O M   I   E   O   A
R   A   N E U T R A L I T Y
A   J   A   S   D   E
L E A R N I N G   S A I D
    C   S   E   H   B
I R K S   M E T A L L I C
N   K   O     V   E   H
L A N D S C A P E S   E
A   I   C   P   N A I V E
I N F L A T E D   L   S
D   E   R   S   S T Y L E
```

173

```
G U S H I N G     H E A R D
R     O   O E   Q   A
I   B A N D A G E   U   M
E     R   T   D R A W S
V A N D A L   P   T
I     A   A W A I T I N G
N   P   T   D   C   R
G R A N D E U R   T   T
  R   R   X   E N A M E L
H E A V Y     V   V   L
O   S   E V A C U E E   I
P   O   A   R   R   N
S O L A R     Y A W N I N G
```

170

```
P E T A L     S   C   O   C
R   R   U N L A W F U L   O
O U N C E   U   I   F   O
P   H A M B U R G E R S   R
E   M   R     O   R   E
L E A N N E S S   B I N D
N   S   E   C   N
N A G S   S T R A I G H T
I   R   E   C   S   R
C O O R D I N A T E   A
E   V   I   E   I C I N G
S K E T C H E S   H   I
T   S   T   D   T O X I C
```

174

```
Q U E A S I E R     L I M P
U   T   S   E   I     A
E V I L   S H A M B L E D
S   A   U   D   E     D
T U S S L E   E   D
S   O   U   F R I S K E D
    W   T   I   N   I
S U S P E C T   K   L   A
O   H   L   C Y C L E D
R   L   A   O   I   U
R E D E S I G N   G I L L
O   G   M   G A   T
W H O M   S P A R R O W S
```

Solutions

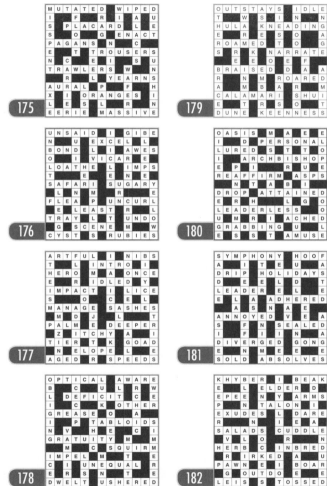

175

176

177

178

179

180

181

182

Solutions

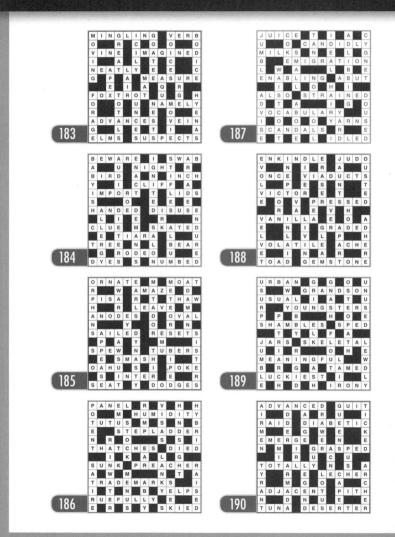

183

M	I	N	G	L	I	N	G				V	E	R	B
O		R		C		O	O		O					O
V	I	N	E		I	M	A	G	I	N	E	D		
I		A		L		T		C			C			I
N	E	A	T	L	Y		E		E		C			C
G		P	A		M	E	A	S	U	R	E			
	E	I		A		Q		R						
F	O	X	T	R	O	T		U		G		H		
O		O		O		N	A	M	E	L	Y			
R		R		T		N		E		O		E		
A	D	V	A	N	C	E	S		V	E	I	N		
G			L		E		T		I			A		
E	L	M	S			S	U	S	P	E	C	T	S	

184

B	E	W	A	R	E		I		S	W	A	B	
A			U		N	I	G	H	T			R	
B	I	R	D		A		N		I	N	C	H	
Y		I		C	L	I	F	F		A			
I	M	P	O	R	T		T		L	I	D	S	
S			O		E		E		E				
H	A	N	D	E	D		D	I	S	U	S	E	
	L		I		E		R			N			
C	L	U	E		M		S	K	A	T	E	D	
E		T	I	A	R	A		L		U			
T	R	E	E		N		L		B	E	A	R	
G													
D	Y	E	S		S		N	U	M	B	E	D	

185

O	R	N	A	T	E		M		M	O	A	T	
R		W		A	M	A	Z	E		D		
P	I	S	A		R		T		T	H	A	W	
H			R		L	E	A	V	E		M		
A	N	O	D	E	S		D		O	V	A	L	
N			Y				O		R		N		
S	A	I	L	E	D		R	E	S	E	T	S	
	P	A		Y			M						
S	P	E	W		T	U	B	E	R	S		
E		S	M	A	S	H		I			T		
O	A	H	U		S		I		P	O	K	E	
S			I	N	T	E	R		E			R	
S	E	A	T		Y		D	O	D	G	E	S	

186

P	A	N	E	L		R		V		H		
O			M		H	U	M	I	D	I	T	Y
T	U	T	U	S		M		S		N		B
E				S	T	E	P	L	A	D	D	E	R
N		R		O		O		S		S		I
T	H	A	T	C	H	E	S		D	I	E	D
		I		K		A		L		G		
S	U	N	K		P	R	E	A	C	H	E	R
A			W		M		N		T			A
T	R	A	D	E	M	A	R	K	S			
I		T		N		B		Y	E	L	P	S
R	U	E	F	U	L	L	Y			E		E
E			R		S		Y		S	K	I	E	D

187

J	U	I	C	E		T		I		A		C
U			O		C	A	N	D	I	D	L	Y
M	I	L	K	S		N		E		L		G
B			E	M	I	G	R	A	T	I	O	N
L		W	A			L		B		E		
E	N	A	B	L	I	N	G		A	B	U	T
		I		L		O		H		I		
A	L	S	O		S	T	R	A	I	N	E	D
D		T		A		I		G				O
V	O	C	A	B	U	L	A	R	Y			U
I		O		O		O		Y	A	R	N	S
S	C	A	N	D	A	L	S		R			E
E			T		E		L		I	D	L	E	D

188

E	N	K	I	N	D	L	E		J	U	D	O
V		N		I		R	A		A		U	
O	N	C	E		V	I	A	D	U	C	T	S
L		P		E		S		N			T	
V	I	C	T	O	R		E	T		E		
E		O	V		P	R	E	S	S	E	D	
R		A		E		V		H				
V	A	N	I	L	L	A		E			O	A
E		L		N		I		G	R	A	D	E	D
L		L		I		L		Y		P		H
V	O	L	A	T	I	L	E		A	C	H	E
E			I		N		A		R			R
T	O	A	D		G	E	M	S	T	O	N	E

189

U	R	B	A	N		G		G		O		U
S			W		G	R	A	N	D	S	O	N
U	S	U	A	L		I		A		T		U
R			Y	O	U	N	G	S	T	E	R	S
P		P		B			H		O			E
S	H	A	M	B	L	E	S		S	P	E	D
	T		Y		L		F		A			
J	A	R	S		S	K	E	L	E	T	A	L
U			I		R			O		H		E
M	E	A	N	I	N	G	F	U	L			W
B		R		G		A		T	A	M	E	D
L	U	C	K	I	E	S	T		I			L
E		H		D		H		I	R	O	N	Y

190

A	D	V	A	N	C	E	D		Q	U	I	T
I		D		A		R		U				I
R	A	I	D		D	I	A	B	E	T	I	C
M			E		G		W		E			K
E	M	E	R	G	E		N		M			E
N		M		I		G	R	A	S	P	E	D
	I		R	U		C		U				
T	O	T	A	L	L	Y		N		S		A
Y		R		E		L	E	C	H	E	R	
R		M		G	O		A		A			C
A	D	J	A	C	E	N	T		P	I	T	H
N		D		N		U		E				
T	U	N	A		D	E	S	E	R	T	E	R

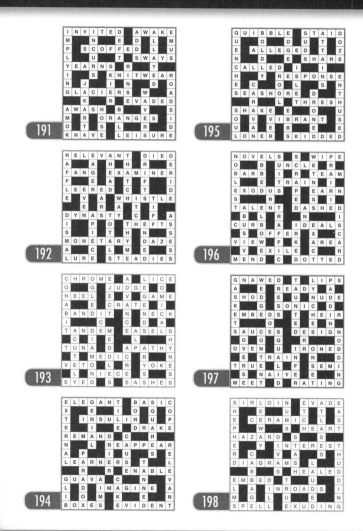

191

```
I N V I T E D   A W A K E
M   N     E     D   L   M
P   S C O F F E D   L   U
L   U     T     S W A Y S
Y E A R N S   R     Y
I   S     K N I T W E A R
N   J     I     N   D   O
G L A C I E R S   W   A
  K     R E V A D E D   S
A W A S H   B     V     I
M   R     O R A N G E S   I
O   T     S     L   R   D
K N A V E   L E I S U R E
```

192

```
R E L E V A N T   D I E D
A   A   H   H     R     E
F A N G   E X A M I N E R
L   E   E   A   T   F   I
L E E R E D   C   T     D
E   V   A   W H I S T L E
    E   R   R   T   I
D Y N A S T Y   C   F   A
I     P   O   T H E F T S
S   M   I   T   H   N   S
M O N E T A R Y   D A Z E
A     C   L   M   E   E S
L U R E   S T E A D I E S
```

193

```
C H R O M E   A   L I C E
O   G   J U D G E   O
H E E L   E   V   G A M E
A   E   C R A T E   I
B A N D I T   N   N E C K
I   C   N   C   D A
T A N D E M   E A S E L S
  C   I   E   L       H
T U N A   D   A P A T H Y
  T   M E D I C   B   N
V E T O   L   R   Y O K E
  L   N I E C E   S   S
E Y E D   S   S A S H E S
```

194

```
E L E G A N T   B A S I C
X   E   I   O   Q   O
T   I N S U L I N   U P
E   I   E   D R A K E
R E M A N D   C   R
N   L   R E A P P E A R
A   P   I   U   S   E
L E A R N E R S   T   L
  R   R   E N A B L E
G U A V A   C   N   V
L   D   I M A G I N E   A
I   O   M   K   E   N
B O X E S   E V I D E N T
```

195

```
Q U I B B L E   S T A I D
U   O   D   U   T   O   Z
E   A L L E G E D   T   Z
N   D   E   S H A R E   I
C A L L E D   I       I
H   K   R E S P O N S E
E   C   O   O   L     S
S E A S H O R E   D   T
H   R   L   T H R E S H
S H A K E   E   O     U
O   V   V I B R A N T   S
U   A   E   K   D   D   E
L O N E R   S K I D D E D
```

196

```
N O V E L S   S   W I P E
O   B   U N C L E   R
B A R B   I   R   T E A M
L   E   T R A I N   P   I
E X O D U S   P   E A R N
S   R   E   S   E S I
T A L E N T   D A S H E D
B   L   R   N     N   I
C U R B   A   I D E A L S
S   O F F E R   X   C
V I E W   F K   A R E A
V   E X I L E   C     R
M E N D   C   D O T T E D
```

197

```
G N A W E D   T   L I P S
A   E   R E A D Y   A
S H O D   E U   N U D E
K   G   S O N I C   D
E M B E D S   T   H E I R
T   O   E E N   N
S A U C E S   D E S I G N
D   O Q   R   O       O
O V E N   U   I R O N E D
E   T R A I N   N   D
T R U E   L F   S E M I
S   N A I V E   E     N
M E E T   D   R A T I N G
```

198

```
S I R L O I N   E V A D E
H   E   U   T   T   A
A   C E R A M I C   L   S
P   W   B   H E A R T   A
H A Z A R D   S   S
E   Y   I N T E R E S T
R C   V   A   S   H   U
D I A G R A M S   T   H
  B   S   H E A L E D
E M B E D   T   U   D
L   A   I N R O A D S   I
M   G   L   U   E   N
S P E L L   E X U D I N G
```

Solutions

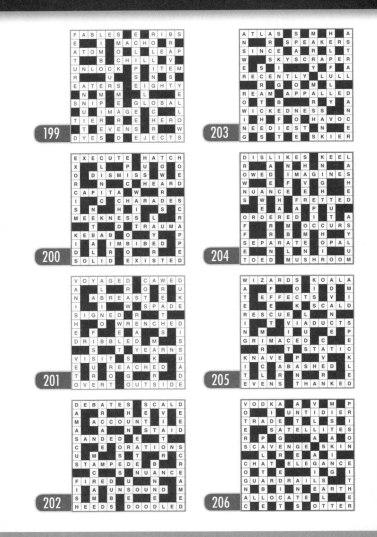

199

200

201

202

203

204

205

206

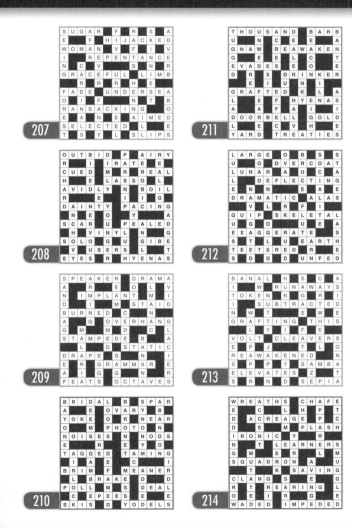

207

208

209

210

211

212

213

214

Solutions

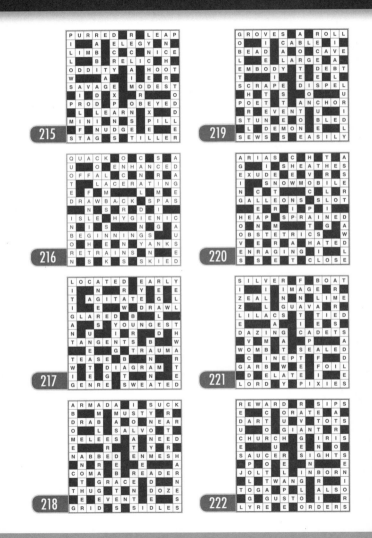

223